Understanding the Scriptures

Student Workbook

The Didache Series

Understanding the Scriptures

Student Workbook

Midwest Theological Forum
Woodridge, Illinois

Published in the United States of America by

Midwest Theological Forum
1420 Davey Road
Woodridge, IL 60517 USA
(630) 739–9750
Fax: (630) 739–9758
Email: mail@mwtf.org
www.theologicalforum.org

Author:	Rev. Fred Gatschet
General Editor:	Rev. James Socias
Associate Editors:	Kimberly D. Chojnicki, Stephen J. Chojnicki, Randal Powers
Editorial Board:	Rev. James Socias, Scott Hahn, Ph.D., Emmet Flood, Kimberly Kirk Hahn, Mike Aquilina
Layout Design:	Kimberly D. Chojnicki

Disclaimer: The editor of this book has attempted to give proper credit to all sources used in the text and illustrations. Any miscredit or lack of credit is unintended and will be corrected in the next edition.

ISBN 978-1-890177-64-5
1-890177-64-4

Printed in Canada

Contents

To the Student:

We live in times of rapid–fire images and sounds. Through television, the internet, cell phones, portable music devices, and the many other means that people (usually those who want to sell us something!) have devised, our senses are bombarded on a minute-by-minute basis. One day the news is full of the fallout from the action of some celebrity. The next day a movie makes its debut, causing a big splash. A few minutes later, a natural disaster has our attention. All of these, at the time they make it into our heads, are made to seem like the most important event in human history. And most of this is just noise. To prove this to yourself, ask yourself the following questions: Who won the award for best actor when you were in the fourth grade? Who won the Super Bowl that year? Who was the Most Valuable Player? What was the greatest natural disaster? If you are like most people, you cannot answer these questions. Now . . . who was your 4th grade teacher? Are you getting a picture as to what is really important in life?

Above all this noise is the Word of God, "living and effective, sharper than any two-edged sword" (Hebrews 4: 12). While our noisy world continues to thrive on the hype of the latest media flash that will be forgotten tomorrow, the Bible continues to be the best selling and most read book of all times and places. Perhaps you have tried to read the Bible before, and quit because it was too confusing. Maybe you have heard bizarre things said about the Book of Revelation. If you are like most Christians, you want to understand the Bible better, but may have been frustrated in your efforts to do so.

My hope for you, as you work through the *Understanding the Scriptures* textbook and this workbook is threefold:

The first is that you learn the epic story of our salvation as God has planned it for us from the beginnings of creation to our own time, living in the Church under the guidance of Jesus Christ as he gloriously reigns in heaven.

The second is based on the first. That is, once you learn this story, when you hear pieces of it read at Mass, you should be able to situate them within the larger story, and then use them as an opportunity to re-visit that part of the story. It is like when you are surfing through the channels on television and see a scene from a favorite movie. Seeing the one scene calls to mind the whole movie. The problem most people have is that they do not know the whole story of the Old and New Testaments, so when they hear the readings proclaimed at Mass, they are just words with little meaning.

Finally, my hope is that once you learn the story of our salvation, you will return often to the Bible to read and re-read these stories that define our faith. *Understanding the Scriptures* is a big book. Once you work your way through it, you will only have been *introduced* to the Word of God. Like any life-long relationship, you will hopefully spend the rest of your life getting better acquainted with it.

May God's Word and the Spirit of Jesus fill you with peace and guide all your thoughts and actions.

Fr. Fred Gatschet
Author, *Understanding the Scriptures Workbook*

Name _____

Date _____

Hour _____

Chapter 1: What is the Bible?

1. The revelation of God in Jesus Christ is transmitted through _____ and

   _____ as one common source.

WHAT CATHOLICS BELIEVE ABOUT THE BIBLE

2. When we say the Scriptures are inspired by the Holy Spirit, what does this mean? Is this to say that the sacred writers were simply taking dictation from the Holy Spirit? Explain.

3. What does it mean when we say that the Bible is inerrant?

4. How does Tradition maintain the integrity of the Bible?

5. On page 8 of the text, there are a number of citations from the *Catechism of the Catholic Church*. These citations mention "the Magisterium" many times. What is "the Magisterium"? (If you do not know, check the vocabulary section on p. 20 of the text.)

6. Who makes up the Magisterium?

7. When we say the pope is infallible, does this mean that he never makes a mistake? What does it mean?

8. St. Jerome was a great biblical scholar who lived in the fourth and the beginning of the fifth centuries. One of his sayings is often quoted: "Ignorance of _____ is ignorance of _____."

HOW THE BIBLE WAS WRITTEN

9. The nature of the Bible is like the nature of Jesus in that both are _____ and _____.

10. The people who wrote the Bible did not have the same understanding of geology, paleontology, and astronomy that we have. How can we say, then, that everything in the Bible is true?

THE BIBLE IS SACRED LITERATURE

11. The text states that we must understand the Bible as *literature*. What does this say, for example, about using the Bible to prove or disprove the existence of the dinosaurs? (Hint: What were the original writers of the Bible thinking when they wrote the ancient texts? Did they know anything about dinosaurs?)

12. When we speak of the Bible as literature, we mean the way it was written. List some of the kinds of literature that we find in the Bible:

THE BIBLE IS RELIGIOUS

13. At times it might appear there are differences between what the Bible says and what modern science proposes. Is there any real conflict here?

14. Why can true religion not be spoken of or described as a purely personal experience?

15. Religion comes from a Latin word which means _____.

16. Explain the impossibility of writing an objective history.

17. Why is Bible history unbiased even though the facts and dates in the Bible do not always agree with the same data collected by other sources?

WHAT "SALVATION HISTORY" IS

18. How is a covenant different from a contract?

19. What is the purpose of the covenants which God made with man throughout history?

20. On page 15 there is a diagram of the six covenants we find in the Bible as Salvation History unfolds. When will the Seventh Covenant occur, and how long will it last?

THE CHURCH WILL BE OUR GUIDE

21. The name of the translation of the Old Testament (Hebrew and some Greek) and the New Testament (Greek) into Latin that was done by St. Jerome is called _____.

22. When we speak of the "Canon of Scripture," we are describing the books that officially make up the Bible. The word "canon" comes from a Greek word that means _____.

HOW THE CANON CAME TO BE

23. Just like today, the liturgy or worship of the ancient Christians consisted of two parts. What are they?

    a.

    b.

24. The word "deuterocanonical" also comes from a Greek word. What does it mean?

25. What role do the deuterocanonical books of the Bible play in Catholic teaching?

26. List two examples of Catholic teachings that come from the deuterocanonical books.

    a.

    b.

27. The translation of the Old Testament from Hebrew into Greek by a team of seventy-two Jewish scholars from 285 to 246 BC is called the _____.

VOCABULARY

Match the following words to their definitions. You should be able to do this with your book closed.

____ Bible/Scripture	____ Canon	____ Catholic
____ Church	____ Covenant	____ Inerrant
____ Infallible	____ Inspired	____ Magisterium
____ Protestant	____ Salvation History	____ Tradition

A. Making no mistakes or errors.

B. The list of inspired books.

C. A Christian not in communion with the Catholic Church.

D. Universal; describing either the Church or one of her members.

E. The collection of all the canonical books.

F. The teaching authority of the Church, which aided by the Holy Spirit, interprets Scripture and Tradition.

G. The living transmission of the message of the Gospel in the Church.

H. Guided by God.

I. The faithful.

J. Incapable of error.

K. The story of God's plan to save us from the consequences of sin.

L. An agreement that establishes a sacred family bond between persons.

Name _____

Date _____

Hour _____

Chapter 2: The Old Testament

1. Why must Christians study the Old Testament?

THE BOOKS OF THE OLD TESTAMENT

2. What are the four main types of writing we find in the Old Testament?

a.

b.

c.

d.

THE LAW

3. The books of the Law are called _____ in Hebrew.

4. Traditionally, _____ is considered to be the author of the five books of the Law, so they are sometimes called the _____.

5. The books of the Law are also called the _____, which comes from a Greek word that means _____.

6. Name at least five of the main characters from the Book of Genesis.

7. The main character in the Book of Exodus is _____.

8. What is the primary story that Exodus tells us?

9. In Greek, Exodus means _____.

10. Why are the laws as written in the Book of Leviticus so explicit in their detail?

11. The book of Numbers begins with a census of all the tribes of Israel who came out of Egypt with Moses. What does this book tell us about the Israelite people?

12. The Ten Commandments appear in which two books of the Bible?

    a.

    b.

13. The name "Deuteronomy" means _____ in Greek.

J, E, D, & P

14. Write the name and the letter that is associated with the name of the theoretical source for the first five books of the Bible.

Name and Letter   *Source*

_____   This source is seen in passages that are thought to represent the perspective of the Jews in Judah in the ninth or eighth century BC.

_____   A later editor who revised all five books of the Pentateuch to reflect the concerns of the Jerusalem priesthood after the return from exile in Babylon.

_____   The source identified in passages that frequently use the Divine Name.

_____   This source is seen also as the author of a book of the Bible that bears the same name, that was written around the seventh century BC during the reforms of King Josiah.

15. While those sources are accepted by many Scripture scholars, can we be sure that this theory is true?

HISTORY

16. Match the historical book of the Bible with the description of its content.

____ Joshua	____ Judges	____ Ruth
____ 1 Samuel	____ 1 Chronicles	____ 1 Kings
____ 2 Samuel	____ 2 Chronicles	____ 2 Kings
____ Ezra	____ Nehemiah	____ Tobit
____ Judith	____ Esther	

A. Much of this book comes from the personal history of the governor who has the same name. It tells how the returning exiles restore the city of Jerusalem and promise to live by the Law of Moses.

B. The story of the woman who becomes the great grandmother of King David, making her also one of the human ancestors of Jesus.

C. The story of how some Jews come back from exile in Babylon, rebuild the temple, and try to restore worship of the One True God.

D. Its two main characters are King Solomon and Elijah the prophet. It describes the building of the first Temple.

E. The story of how the Israelites under Moses' successor begin the conquest of the Promised Land.

F. Tells much the same story as 1 and 2 Samuel, but emphasizes the religious nature of David's reign as king, and his preparations for the building of the Temple.

G. The story of a pious man who, even while in exile, scrupulously follows the Law of Moses.

H. The tragic story of Saul, the first king of Israel.

I. The story of an heroic woman who saves Israel by a clever strategy that succeeds because of her trust in God.

J. A retelling of the events of 1 and 2 Kings with most of the emphasis on the kingdom of Judah.

K. Tells of the Israelite people's attempts to finish conquering the Promised Land after the death of Joshua, and how they fail because of their continual disobedience of God.

L. Tells the story of God's everlasting covenant with David.

M. Tells how the divided Kingdoms of Israel and Judah fall away from God and turn to idols and God finally allowing them to be conquered and destroyed.

N. The story of a heroic Israelite woman who becomes the queen of Persia.

WISDOM

17. Which of the Wisdom Books . . .

. . . is a poem in praise of wisdom with a long commentary on how patient God has been with human folly? _____

. . . is a collection of sayings attributed to King Solomon? _____

. . . describes for us how to live a good life in the world without compromising our faith in God? _____

. . . is a long poem that asks the hard question: Why does God let bad things happen to good people? _____

... speaks about "vanity," and that little faith can be placed in things of this world; the only thing a person should do is to trust in God? _____

... contains poems and songs that we use every day in Mass? _____

... is the world's greatest love poem? _____

PROPHECY

18. What kind of messages did God's prophets bring to his people? (The text gives two.)

19. List the Major Prophets.

    a.

    b.

    c.

20. Why are the "minor prophets" referred to as such?

21. Who are the last three prophets who came after the Jews returned from exile in Babylon?

    a.

    b.

    c.

22. Complete the crossword by finding the names of the prophets described in the clues.

ACROSS

3 Pronounced God's judgment against the whole earth, not just Judah and Israel. (9)

6 Brought a stern warning to Israel at a time of great prosperity. (4)

8 "See, your king comes to you, humble and riding on an ass, on a colt, the foal of an ass." (9)

9 The shortest book in the Old Testament. (7)

10 Foretold the destruction of Judah and called upon the people to repent. (8)

14 "Return to the Lord, your God, for he is gracious and merciful, slow to anger and abounding in steadfast love." (4)

15 A book of poems attributed to Jeremiah bemoaning the destruction of Jerusalem. (12)

17 Led the effort to rebuild the Temple in Jerusalem after the Exile. (6)

18 Foretold the end of Nineveh, the capital of the Assyrian Empire. (5)

DOWN

1 These two books tell of the revolts of pious Jews against the influences of the Greeks. (9)

2 Pronounced judgment against the wicked, and comfort to the righteous who live by faith. (8)

4 His marriage to an unfaithful wife is a metaphor for God's relationship with his unfaithful people Israel. (5)

5 Pronounced judgment against those who take bribes and exploit the poor; foretells that the Savior will be born in Bethlehem. (5)

7 Perhaps written in Babylon by a disciple of Jeremiah, prophesying about a New Covenant. (6)

11 Foretold the destruction of Jerusalem, but also offered hope that God could bring Israel back to life. (7)

12 Warned the returned exiles that God was not pleased with offerings made from ill-gotten goods. (7)

13 The story of a Jewish prophet who gained a high place in Babylon during the Exile. (6)

14 The story of a reluctant prophet that gives us a good idea as to what it would be like to be God's chosen prophet. (5)

16 This prophet gave us some of the clearest prophecies about the coming of Jesus. (6)

WHAT TYPOLOGY IS AND HOW IT WORKS

23. What is a "type" in the biblical sense of the word?

24. Explain how typology works.

25. Below are some events from the Old Testament that are commonly accepted as "types" for events in the New Testament and life in the Church. What are they?

OLD TESTAMENT EVENT	NEW TESTAMENT EVENT OR CHURCH PRACTICE
The near sacrifice of Isaac by Abraham	The sacrifice of Jesus on the cross.
The Israelite people crossing from slavery to freedom through the waters of the Red Sea	
"And Melchizedek king of Salem brought out bread and wine; he was priest of God Most High" (Genesis 14: 18)	

Name _____

Date _____

Hour _____

Chapter 3: The Creation of the World

1. What is the purpose of the creation story, and what literary forms does it use?

DAYS 1-3: CREATING FORM

2. What are the three forms that God creates in the first three days of his work?

   a.

   b.

   c.

DAYS 4-6: FILLING THE VOID

3. What does Genesis describe as the rulers of time?

4. What does Genesis describe as the rulers of space?

5. Who does God create to rule life, and how is this to be accomplished?

CREATION: A COVENANT WITH THE UNIVERSE

6. How exactly does God go about creating? What are his raw materials?

7. The textbook describes God's Word with a capital "W." What does this mean? (See John 1: 1-5.)

8. The text tells us that God first creates forms and then fills them with inhabitants. Someone unfamiliar with Hebrew poetry might say that the creation story makes no sense because light is created three days before the sun. Using the plan proposed in the text, how would you answer this?

9. What does it mean in Hebrew to say, "I swear a covenant"?

10. What is the significance of the Sabbath rest, given your answer in Question #9?

11. What is the effect of the Sabbath rest on God's creation?

UNDERSTANDING TIME AS A PART OF CREATION

12. Consider the following diagram.

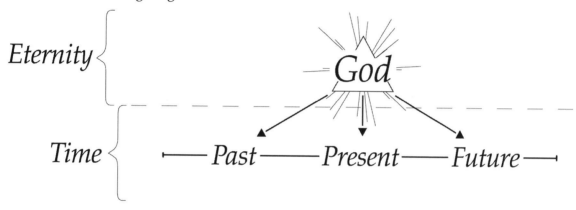

What do we mean when we say that God is eternal?

13. Jesus says, "Whatever you do to the least of my brethren, you do for me." How can this be literally true?

CREATION IS GOOD

14. Someone might say that if we sin sexually with our bodies, that the body is evil. Others might say that some things in the created order (like money) are evil. What does the Book of Genesis say about this way of thinking?

15. How do the sacraments of the Church reinforce God's pronouncement that creation is good?

IS IT TRUE?

16. In our day there is a lot of discussion about whether the Bible's account of creation can be believed as true. How would you answer this?

CREATION OF HUMAN BEINGS IN THE IMAGE OF GOD

17. What is it about human nature that makes us most like God?

18. What is the mistake we often make in placing value on people? What is the basis of our value as persons?

19. What gives our work dignity?

20. What were some of the gifts Adam and Eve had before they sinned?

THE MARRIAGE COVENANT

21. When did God create marriage?

22. Why can human beings not dissolve a marriage?

23. What are some terms that describe the very nature of marriage?

GOD OUR FATHER

24. When the name "Elohim" is being used to describe God, which of his attributes does the biblical writer wish to emphasize?

25. When the name "Yahweh" or "Lord" is being used to describe God, which of his attributes does the biblical writer wish to emphasize?

26. If all of God's creation is meant to be a temple, who is the priest?

THE FALL

27. What does the Hebrew term *nahash* tell us about the nature of the serpent who tricked Adam and Eve?

SPIRITUAL DEATH

28. The woman tells the serpent that she and her husband may not eat of the tree in the middle of the garden or they will die. The serpent says that they will not die. Who is telling the truth, and what does this tell us about the nature of temptations in general?

29. The text marks a difference between "natural life" and "supernatural life." The Book of Revelation states, "*But as for the cowardly, the faithless, the polluted, as for murderers, fornicators, sorcerers, idolaters, and all liars, their lot shall be in the lake that burns with fire and brimstone, which is the second death*" (21: 8). If there is a "second death," there must be a "first death." Using the terminology from the textbook what is the "first death"?

What is the "second death"?

30. Having sinned against God, what do Adam and Eve do?

WHERE ARE YOU?

31. We saw earlier in this chapter (Understanding Time as a Part of Creation), that God is in all places and in all times. If God was present when Adam and Eve sinned, why does he ask, "Where are you?"

32. How does Adam respond when caught in his sin?

33. How does Eve respond for her part in the sin?

THE FIRST GOSPEL

34. In Genesis 3: 15, we find the first hint of the coming of the Messiah. In Latin, the name of this "First Gospel" is _____.

THE CURSE

35. What are four negative consequences of the sin of Adam and Eve?

     a.

     b.

     c.

     d.

36. According to the *Catechism of the Catholic Church* (404) what exactly do we inherit from Adam and Eve?

37. Explain the consequences of Original Sin.

EVIL

38. What is envy?

39. Why did Cain kill Abel?

40. We have seen in Genesis 3 the true nature of sin and temptation. Commonly (and sometimes comically) we see in movies, television, and cartoons, a little devil standing on someone's left shoulder enticing them to do evil, and a little angel on the person's right shoulder trying to persuade them to do good. While this makes for lively entertainment, it has very little to do with real life. Below, mark each scenario that is most like the temptation of Adam and Eve.

_____ Julio is in the music store and sees a CD that he would like, but he does not have enough money. He is tempted to steal it.

_____ Joseph Stalin once said, "One death is a tragedy. A million deaths is a statistic."

_____ Sarah works as an underpaid waitress, and often takes money from the cash register and undercharges her friends when they come into the restaurant. She figures the owner owes it to her.

_____ It really bothers Fabian that he has cut off most contact with his family.

_____ Michael often struggles with thoughts of impure sexual acts.

_____ Louise is a pregnant teenager and has contemplated having an abortion.

_____ Kevin has no problem viewing pornography on the internet, since he is in the privacy of his own home.

_____ Planned Parenthood, and other groups advocating "reproductive rights" routinely make their way into the world of young people to "educate them about their choices."

CREATION AND EVOLUTION

41. Is the theory, or are theories of evolution necessarily in conflict with the Bible? (Refer back to the section "Is it True?" if necessary.)

42. What is one of the areas where the theory of evolution is in conflict with the Faith, and why is it a point of conflict?

VOCABULARY

Using the vocabulary list for this chapter (text, p. 63), find each term in the grid below.

```
F  V  P  G  Y  I  I  G  U  A  A  V  P  G  Y  G  M  H  F  K  G  L
Q  A  O  V  H  M  M  H  J  Z  Q  G  O  V  H  T  C  V  V  L  L  F
A  H  T  C  N  K  A  J  M  V  A  H  I  C  N  R  P  C  B  P  K  D
S  N  U  H  H  R  G  K  N  O  S  N  U  X  U  H  L  X  G  W  I  S
D  S  Y  S  E  V  E  L  H  I  D  S  Y  H  J  N  I  Z  E  Z  U  A
E  A  T  W  K  R  B  M  Y  D  E  A  C  W  K  M  K  A  L  S  J  Z
H  P  R  Q  L  B  S  N  T  M  H  E  V  O  L  U  T  I  O  N  M  V
G  L  E  A  P  G  M  O  F  K  H  L  E  A  P  E  A  P  H  X  J  Y
H  K  W  Z  O  T  A  V  F  T  S  N  U  X  H  N  I  Z  I  Z  H  A
S  E  R  P  E  N  T  C  F  T  D  S  Y  S  J  M  K  A  M  S  G  H
K  H  A  O  G  H  L  O  G  W  H  A  T  W  K  J  J  Q  W  D  H  W
L  G  S  L  F  N  S  Z  S  Z  H  E  R  Q  L  A  V  P  G  Y  J  E
P  F  D  K  D  R  A  A  S  G  L  C  R  E  A  T  I  O  N  K  H
O  D  F  I  O  J  J  Q  B  D  H  K  W  H  O  A  H  I  C  N  L  G
D  S  Y  T  J  F  V  L  B  R  D  S  Y  S  U  N  I  Z  T  Z  U  A
E  B  C  W  K  V  B  M  A  D  A  M  T  W  K  R  K  A  E  S  J  Z
H  O  R  Q  L  B  N  N  T  M  H  P  R  Q  L  J  C  Q  W  D  M  V
D  V  P  G  Y  G  M  B  H  K  G  L  J  Q  P  J  Y  H  C  B  E  D
P  R  O  T  O  E  V  A  N  G  E  L  I  U  M  G  H  L  X  G  W  N
```

Name _____

Date _____

Hour _____

Chapter 4: The Early World

THE EVIL LINE OF CAIN

1. Cain is banished by God for murdering Abel. He goes to the land of "Nod" which means

   _____.

2. In the land of Nod, Cain has a son and builds a city. He names both of them _____.

3. Cain's descendants are credited with originating most of the things that make civilization possible. Read Genesis beginning at 4: 17. Identify with which profession each of the following of Cain's ancestors are credited:

   a. Jabal   _____

   b. Jubal   _____

   c. Tubal-cain   _____

4. Seven generations after Adam, _____ is born. He breaks God's covenant by

   practicing _____.

5. According to the teachings of Jesus, Christians are to practice _____ as often as

   Lamech practiced _____ on those who would harm him.

THE RIGHTEOUS LINE OF SETH

6. The name of Seth's son is _____.

7. When the Book of Genesis (4: 26) says that *"men began to call upon the name of the LORD,"* what does it mean?

8. What is the difference between the actions of Cain and his descendants and those of Seth?

9. In Genesis 5: 3, we read *"When Adam had lived a hundred and thirty years, he became the father of a son in his own likeness, after his image, and named him Seth."* Here, the author of Genesis uses the same words (image . . . and likeness) that were used to describe the creation of Man. What does this mean?

THE SONS OF GOD AND THE DAUGHTERS OF MEN

10. So far, we have seen the family of Cain as being primarily wicked, while Seth's family remained faithful to God. Yet Seth's family is not perfect either. Why?

11. Genesis 6 opens with the verse, *"When men began to multiply on the face of the ground, and daughters were born to them, the sons of God saw that the daughters of men were fair and they took to wife such of them as they chose."*

    Who are "the sons of God"? _____

    Who are "the daughters of men"? _____

12. According to the text, what is the major violation of God's covenant that results from the union of the "sons of God" with the "daughters of men"?

THE FLOOD

13. What is the net result of the intermixing of the lines of Seth and Cain?

14. Why does God choose Noah to be the beginning of a new start for humanity, *and more importantly, what does this teach us today?*

15. We see the number "seven" often in the story of Noah. Biblically speaking, what does "seven" mean?

16. When we see the number "forty" in the Bible, what is it usually describing?

17. After the flood waters receded, where did Noah's Ark come to rest?

18. With regard to his family and God, what role did Noah have after the flood?

DID THE FLOOD REALLY HAPPEN?

19. What is the setting for the flood as described in the book *Noah's Flood*?

20. Regardless of any theory, what is the essential point of the story of the Great Flood?

THE COVENANT WITH NOAH

21. What is the parallelism between God's promises to Adam and his promises to Noah?

22. What is God's main promise in the Covenant he makes with Noah?

23. What is the sign of God's Covenant with Noah?

24. How is the Great Flood a "type" of Baptism?

ANOTHER STORY OF THE FLOOD

25. What is the main difference between the Gilgamesh story of a great flood, and the story of Noah?

THE CURSE ON CANAAN

26. Once the flood was over, what profession did Noah take up?

27. What does Ham do, and why is it so bad?

28. What is the result of Ham's actions?

29. What remarkable trait do Shem and Abraham both share in the Old Testament?

30. What does the word "shem" mean in Hebrew?

THE ARROGANCE OF THE CHILDREN OF HAM

31. What do all of the clans who are descendants of Ham have in common?

32. Where does the word or name "Hebrew" come from?

33. What is the sin of the builders of the Tower of Babel?

34. In Genesis 11: 3, the children of Ham say, "... 'Come, let us make bricks, and burn them thoroughly.' And they had brick for stone, and bitumen for mortar." Give examples of how people in our time use technology to bring about a desired effect that is contrary to God's will.

THE REAL TOWER OF BABEL

35. What is the name of the pyramid-shaped structures found in Mesopotamia?

VOCABULARY

Study the vocabulary words and definitions from this chapter. With your book closed, unscramble the following words. Place the unscrambled words in the boxes provided.

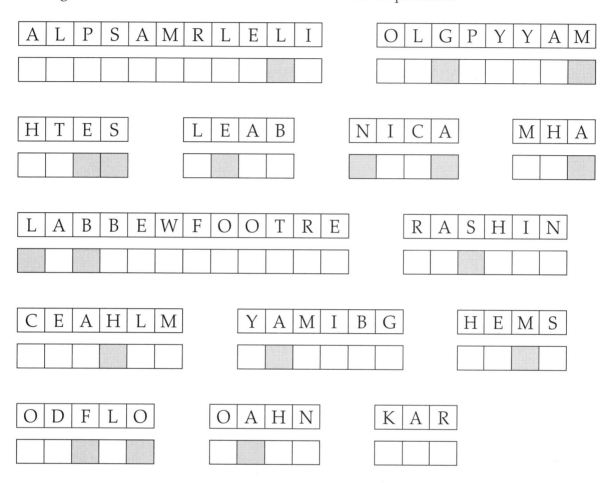

Unscramble the letters from the shaded boxes to reveal a phrase from the ninth chapter of Genesis.

Name _____

Date _____

Hour _____

Chapter 5: Abraham, Our Father

1. Abraham comes from the descendants of Noah's son _____.

2. Before God gives him the name Abraham, he is known as _____.

3. Abraham's name comes from two Hebrew words "Ab" and "raham." Together these words mean _____.

THE LIFE OF A NOMAD

4. Before being called by God, Abram lived in _____ which was an ancient city in _____.

5. Abraham's father _____ raises Abraham's other brothers _____ and _____ as well as Abraham's nephew _____.

6. When does Abraham's story really begin?

THE PROMISES TO ABRAM

7. God makes a series of promises to Abraham. What is each promise, and when is it fulfilled?

Promise	Fulfilled

8. What precisely does God mean when he promises that through Abraham all the families on earth shall be blessed?

9. Referring to Abraham and other great men of faith from the Old Testament, the Letter to the Hebrews (11: 13) states: *"These all died in faith, not having received what was promised, but having seen it and greeted it from afar."* How does this apply specifically to Abraham?

1. GOD'S OATH: LAND AND A NATION

10. What are three things that would make God's promises to Abraham hard to accept?

    a.

    b.

    c.

11. Explain how oaths were sworn in the ancient Near East.

12. How are these details reflected in the oath that God makes to Abraham?

2. GOD'S OATH: KINGSHIP AND A NAME

13. At this point, Abraham and Sarah are still known as Abram and Sarai. They are having a hard time believing in God's promise of many descendants. Sarai tells her husband to have relations with one of the slave girls in order to have a son by her. What was the slave girl's name?

14. They named the boy born of Abram and the slave girl _____.

15. When he is ninety-three years old, God appears again to Abram and changes his name to Abraham. At this point, God confirms the second part of his covenant with Abraham. What is it?

16. What is the external sign of this covenant?

17. God also changes Sarai's name to _____ which means _____.

18. By the grace of God, Abraham and Sarah, in their old age, have a son whom they name

_____ which means _____. They gave him this name because . . .

19. What is the significance of Ishmael being circumcised when he was thirteen years old?

SODOM AND GOMORRAH

20. In Genesis 18: 20, God says, *"Because the outcry against Sodom and Gomorrah is great and their sin is very grave, I will go down to see whether they have done altogether according to the outcry which has come to me; and if not, I will know."* Does God not know what is happening some place on earth? What does this mean?

21. Why does Abraham try to "bargain" with God regarding the destruction of Sodom and Gomorrah?

22. When the two angels get to Sodom, what happens to them?

23. Read the blue sections of the *Catechism of the Catholic Church* on pages 95-96 of the text and answer the following questions.
    - After centuries of various cultures struggling with the issue of homosexuality, what, according to the *Catechism*, are the psychological causes?

- The *Catechism* states that homosexual actions are "acts of great depravity" (*Catechism* 2357), and that they are contrary to natural law. What does this mean? (cf. Romans 1: 18-32)

- What does it mean to say that homosexual acts close the sexual act to the gift of life?

- What does it mean to say that homosexual acts are not sexually complimentary?

- What does it mean to say that homosexual acts are "intrinsically disordered"?

- The Church has always taught that there is a difference between the sin and the sinner. What does the Church teach about how we are to deal with homosexual persons?

- How does the Church direct homosexual persons to lead their lives?

24. Why is the intended rape of Lot's visitors doubly horrendous?

25. What happened to Lot's wife as they fled from Sodom?

26. The nations of the _____ and the _____, who became enemies

of the Israelites, were born from the incestuous union of Lot and his daughters.

3. THE BINDING OF ISAAC AND GOD'S THIRD OATH

27. What happens to Ishmael and his mother Hagar?

28. How do both Abraham and Isaac respond to God's call to sacrifice Isaac?

29. What is the essential message of the near-sacrifice of Isaac?

30. How can we understand Isaac to be a "type" for Jesus?

ISAAC	CHRIST

VOCABULARY

31. Changing his name from _____, God named him _____ from the Hebrew words "father of a multitude."

32. Changing her name from _____, God named her _____ from a Hebrew word that means "princess" or "queen."

33. Two cities of great depravity destroyed by God

were _____ and _____.

34. Abraham's sons, _____ and _____ are half-brothers.

35. Abraham's home town, _____, was located in Mesopotamia.

36. Abraham's nephew _____ received two _____ into his home

who warned him to flee from the city which was about to be destroyed by God.

37. The near-sacrifice of Isaac took place on Mount _____.

38. The visible sign of the covenant that God made with Abraham is called _____.

Chapter 6: The Patriarchs

1. What were some of the differences between Abraham and the Canaanites?

2. Why was Abraham absolutely insistent that his son Isaac not marry a Canaanite woman?

FINDING A WIFE FOR ISAAC

3. Abraham's servant goes back to Mesopotamia in search of a wife for Isaac. Where does he first encounter Isaac's bride-to-be?

4. The name of Isaac's bride-to-be is _____.

5. The servant prays that God will guide him in finding the right woman for Isaac. How does this happen?

6. How is Rebekah related to Abraham?

7. Who is Rebekah's brother, and why is he important?

JACOB AND ESAU

8. How do Isaac and Rebekah respond to one another when they meet?

9. What two things are remarkable about Rebekah's only pregnancy?

    a.

    b.

10. What is the name of the first of Isaac and Rebekah's sons, and why did they name him as such?

11. What was the name of their second son, and why did he get this name?

12. "When the boys grew up, Esau was a skillful hunter, a man of the field, while Jacob was a quiet man, dwelling in tents. Isaac loved _____, because he ate of his game; but Rebekah loved _____." (Genesis 25: 27-28)

13. Based on the text and Genesis 25: 27-34, describe Esau.

14. What kind of a man was Jacob?

15. How do Jacob and his mother Rebekah plot to get the inheritance away from Esau?

JACOB'S LADDER

16. What happens as a result of Jacob "supplanting" his brother Esau?

17. What is the significance of Jacob's dream about the ladder going up to heaven?

18. When Jacob woke up from his dream, what did he call the place where he had the dream, and what does its name mean?

JACOB AND LABAN

19. Jacob fits in very quickly with his uncle Laban and his family. At first he is working for Laban at no charge, but then Laban insists on paying him. What does Jacob want for his work, and what more does he promise in addition to the work he has already done?

20. At the end of the previous section we were told that Jacob would get a taste of his own medicine. How does this happen?

21. For Jacob to get what he wants, what does he have to do?

TWELVE SONS

22. What usually happens when we read about polygamy in the Bible?

23. What is the bitter irony of Jacob's two wives?

24. How does Rachel seek to rectify the situation at first, and where have we seen this before?

25. What are the names of the boys to whom Rachel finally gives birth (cf. Genesis 35: 24)?

    a.

    b.

26. As Jacob and Laban are still trying to take advantage of each other, how does Jacob finally come out ahead?

27. At this point, Jacob takes his wealth and family and makes his escape from Laban. What must he face from his past?

THE TWELVE TRIBES OF ISRAEL

28. When the Promised Land is finally divided up among the twelve Tribes of Israel in the Book of Joshua, neither the tribe of Joseph nor Levi get any land. Yet it is still divided up twelve ways. How does this happen?

WRESTLING WITH GOD: JACOB NAMED ISRAEL

29. Jacob spends the night wrestling with the angel of God, and wins the contest. The angel gives

    Jacob the name of _____**Israel**_____ which means . . .

30. In the end, what happens between Jacob and Esau?

JOSEPH'S BROTHERS SELL HIM AS A SLAVE

31. Why do you think that Joseph was Jacob's (Israel's) favorite son?

32. What are the three translations that describe the coat that Jacob gave to Joseph?

    a.

    b.

    c.

33. Describe Joseph's two dreams.

    a.

    b.

34. What do these two dreams mean?

35. When Joseph's brothers plot to kill him, who tries to save him?

36. What ultimately happens to Joseph?

GOD TURNS EVIL INTO AN INSTRUMENT OF SALVATION

37. What does Joseph do that indebts all of Egypt to him?

38. How do Joseph and his brothers first come into contact with each other years after they sold him as a slave?

39. Describe the meetings between Joseph and his brothers (cf. Genesis 42-45).

40. Keeping in mind Joseph is the second most powerful man in the known world, how do his brothers respond when Joseph reveals himself to them?

41. After the drama of revealing himself to his brothers, what does Joseph do?

42. How is Joseph a "type" of Christ?

VOCABULARY

Study the vocabulary word list for this chapter (text, p. 125). Without looking at your text, use the clues given below to fill in the grid provided. The answer to the last question will be revealed from the shaded boxes.

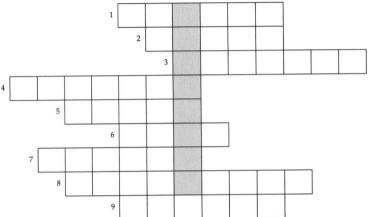

1. The land which God promised to give to Abraham's descendants, covering about the same territory as the modern country of Israel. (6)

2. The younger of Isaac and Rebekah's twin sons. (5)

3. The title of the King of Egypt. (7)

4. Isaac's wife. (7)

5. During the time of Abraham, Isaac, and Jacob, this ancient kingdom along the Nile River was the wealthiest and most powerful nation on earth. (5)

6. The elder of Isaac and Rebekah's twin sons. (4)

7. The name given to Jacob after he wrestled with the angel, and the name of the nation that descended from him. (6)

8. The title given to Abraham, Isaac, and Jacob. (9)

9. Jacob's favorite son who, after being sold by his brothers as a slave, rose to become second only to the Pharaoh in his position of authority. (6)

The name of Jacob's son is _____ .

Name _____

Date _____

Hour _____

Chapter 7: The Exodus

1. What are the Israelites doing as the Book of Exodus begins?

THE BIRTH AND RESCUE OF MOSES

2. What does the Book of Exodus mean when it states, "Now there arose a new king in Egypt who did not know Joseph"?

3. How does the new Pharaoh stir up public sentiment against the Israelites?

4. What is the first stage of Pharaoh's plan to keep the Israelites under control?

5. What is the second stage, and why does this evil proposition make sense?

6. From Exodus 2: 10 and from our text, we find out the meaning of Moses' name. What is it?

MOSES REBELS

7. God's hand is at work in Moses' life. What are some of the details by which the Egyptians unwittingly contribute to their own defeat?

8. What is the event that pushes Moses to claim his Hebrew ancestry?

9. What causes Moses to flee Egypt?

10. While in the land of Midian, Moses marries _____ the daughter of a priest

named _____.

THE BURNING BUSH: GOD REVEALS HIS NAME TO MOSES

11. How old is Moses when he meets God on the mountain for the first time?

12. How does God identify himself to Moses in the Burning Bush?

13. If God had only identified himself as the God of Abraham, who else could claim him as their God?

14. If God had only identified himself as the God of Abraham and Isaac, who else could claim him as their God?

15. What is the cryptic phrase that contains the Name of God?

16. Why does God often choose those who are weak and with few apparent skills or abilities to do his work?

THE MESSAGE TO PHARAOH

17. How does God plan to use Israel as a priestly nation?

18. What is Moses' first demand to Pharaoh?

THE PLAGUES

(Read chapters 7-11 of the Book of Exodus to see the details of the Plagues and the attitudes of Pharaoh and his officials.)

19. What is Pharaoh's attitude toward God when he says, *"Who is the Lord, that I should heed his voice and let Israel go? I do not know the Lord, and moreover, I will not let Israel go"* (Exodus 5: 2) What does he mean by this?

20. How does Pharaoh respond to Moses' first demand that the people be allowed to go to the desert to sacrifice to God?

21. Why is Pharaoh unimpressed with Moses' staff turning into a snake (cf. Exodus 7: 8-12), the Nile turning into blood (cf. Exodus 7: 22), and the plague of the frogs (cf. Exodus 8: 7)?

22. After the plagues of the gnats and then of the flies, Pharaoh seems willing to negotiate. He proposes that Moses and the people may have their sacrifice, but that they must stay within the land of Egypt for the festival (cf. Exodus 8: 25). Why does Moses insist to Pharaoh that the sacrifices cannot take place within the land of Egypt?

23. How are the plagues themselves God's judgments upon the gods of Egypt?

24. When God is talking to Moses through the Burning Bush, he says, *"I know that the king of Egypt will not let you go unless compelled by a mighty hand"* (Ex 3: 19). How does Pharaoh play right into God's hand?

THE PASSOVER

25. In a final act of judgment on Pharaoh and the Egyptians, God tells Moses that his Angel will pass through the land and slay the first born of all the Egyptians and their livestock. What will God prove by doing this?

26. How were the Israelites to identify their homes so that the Angel of Death would pass over them?

27. Why did God command the Israelites to eat unleavened bread with their Passover meal?

THE PASSOVER LAMB AS A TYPE OF CHRIST

28. How are we to understand the Passover lamb as a type of Christ?

29. The Jewish people celebrated the Passover for over 1000 years before the birth of Jesus. How is this part of God's magnificent and intricate plan for our salvation?

30. One of the great ironies of the story is that the Israelites do not simply gain their freedom and walk away. What happens?

ESCAPE FROM EGYPT

31. Why do Pharaoh and his officials change their minds about letting the Israelites go?

32. With Pharaoh and his army following, the Israelites arrive at the Sea of Reeds, which in English translations of the Bible is often rendered as _____.

33. How does God clear a path through the Sea of Reeds for the Israelites?

34. What happens when the Egyptians try to follow the Israelites through the Sea?

35. What are some difficulties that await the Israelites?

SPIRITUAL FOOD IN THE WILDERNESS

36. Once free, what is the first concern and complaint of the Israelites?

37. How does God provide for their needs?

38. Numbers 11: 4-6 describes the attitude of the Israelites after having been taken care of by God in the wilderness: *"... the people of Israel also wept again, and said, 'O that we had meat to eat! We remember the fish we ate in Egypt for nothing, the cucumbers, the melons, the leeks, the onions, and the garlic;* **but now our strength is dried up, and there is nothing at all but this manna to look at'"** (emphasis added). What aspect of human nature does this Scripture illustrate for us?

39. What does the Hebrew word "manna" mean in English?

40. How is the manna that God sends down on the Israelites in the desert a type for the Sacrament of the Eucharist?

THE COVENANT AT SINAI

41. According to God's plan, what is to be the priestly function of the People of Israel?

42. List the Ten Commandments.

1.

2.

3.

4.

5.

6.

7.

8.

9.

10.

43. God had promised that he would speak to his people face-to-face. What happens when he tries to do this?

44. How does God keep his covenant promise with Israel?

THE DECALOGUE AND THE NATURAL LAW

45. The Ten Commandments are also called the _____ which means
_____.

46. The Ten Commandments form a unity of morality that ties our religious relationship with God to our social relationship to our neighbor.

    a. The first three commandments deal with what?

    b. The next seven commandments deal with what?

47. What is the Natural Law, and what is an example of it?

48. How are the Ten Commandments a privileged expression of the Natural Law?

THE TEMPLE IN HEAVEN AND ON EARTH

49. How long is Moses alone with God on Mt. Sinai?

50. What does God show Moses during this time?

51. What is the Ark of the Covenant? What two purposes did it serve?

VOCABULARY

Study the vocabulary terms on page 146.

With your book closed, complete the puzzle.

Answers are diagonal up and diagonal down (always written left to right).

DIAGONAL UP

4 Moses' brother. (5)

6 The mountain where Moses received the Law from God. (5)

7 The body of water that God parted so that the Israelites could escape the Egyptians. (6)

10 A miraculous food that it is a type for the Eucharist. (5)

12 The ornate box representing God's throne on earth that held the tablets of the Law. (16)

13 From a Greek word that means "going out." (6)

14 A series of rulers from the same family. (7)

15 A woman who assists other women to give birth to their children. (7)

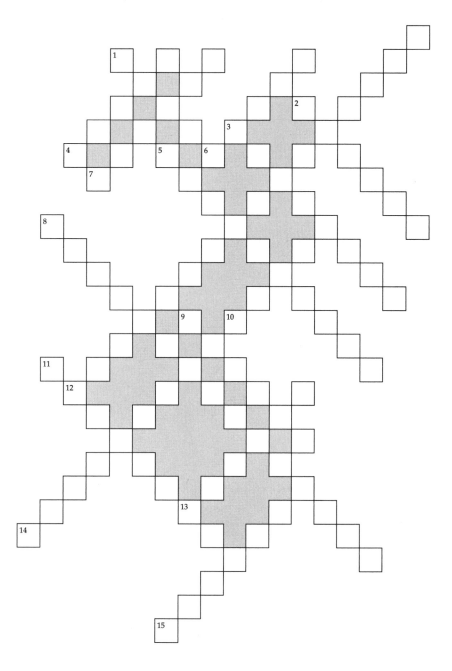

DIAGONAL DOWN

1 Chosen by God to lead the Israelites out of Egypt. (5)

2 The name used by the Egyptians to describe the Israelites and the related tribes. (6)

3 Worshipping man-made images as though they were gods. (8)

5 The tent that served as a meeting place and temple for the Israelites while they wandered in the desert. (10)

8 The Decalogue. (15)

9 God sent ten of this disaster upon Egypt in order to convince Pharaoh to let the Hebrews leave. (6)

11 The saving of the firstborn of Israel while the firstborn of the Egyptians was killed. (8)

Name _____

Date _____

Hour _____

Chapter 8: The Law

1. Back in Genesis, we saw how God created everything including humanity, as being good. What was God's original plan for us before the sin of Adam and Eve?

2. What destroys God's plan for us?

3. Once God rescued his people from Egypt, what was his plan for them?

   A nation of priests; each father a priest in his own house

4. What act of the Israelites demonstrates their distrust for God's plan?

   Worshipping Golden calf.

5. What is the result of this sin?

   The shattering of the Law, Drinking Gold water. Deaths of 3,000. Institution of priesthood,

6. How does this very same dynamic take place in our lives as individuals and as societies?

   When we as individuals or nations defy gods just laws, we suffer.

7. As Moses gives the people the "Second Law" in the Book of Deuteronomy, what two prophecies does he make?

    a. *They will break it.*

    b.

8. As God's plan unfolds throughout the ages, what is the indispensable function of the Old Law?

    to be purified & perfected in new covenant

THE GOLDEN CALF CHANGES ISRAEL'S RELATIONSHIP WITH GOD

9. What did the Exodus do for the Israelites?

    Declaration of Independence

10. Exodus 32 is filled with bitter irony. The Israelites had seen the ten plagues and had crossed through the Red Sea. What unimaginable statements do the Israelites make about God?

    Who has brought us out of Egypt

11. Why did the people demand Aaron make them a golden calf? Why not some other god from Egypt or Canaan?

    God of Fertility, Returning to immoral practice.

12. What effect does this have on the covenant that they had just made with God?

    Shows lack of faith

THE INSTITUTION OF THE PRIESTHOOD

13. Meanwhile, as God and Moses are talking on the mountain, what does God tell Moses about the Israelites, and how does he refer to them?

a stiffnecked people who worship other gods

14. What does God initially propose to Moses as a solution to the behavior of the Israelites?

destroy them - Make Moses the new Abraham.

15. How does Moses respond to this idea?

Asks instead that he be blotted out. Warns God that the Egyptians will call God unfaithful

16. When Moses sees for himself what is going on in the Israelite camp, what does he do?

Smashes the tablets of law. Grinds gold into water, Gives du Business → Aaron

17. In Exodus 32: 20 we read, *"[Moses] took the calf which they had made, burnt it with fire, and ground it to powder, and scattered it upon the water, and made the people of Israel drink it."* Why do you think Moses would do this? What would you do if you took a gulp of water that had metal dust in it?

18. As we continue with Exodus 32: 21-24 we read, *"And Moses said to Aaron, 'What did this people do to you that you have brought a great sin upon them?' And Aaron said, 'Let not the anger of my lord burn hot; you know the people, that they are set on evil. For they said to me, 'Make us gods, who shall go before us; as for this Moses, the man who brought us up out of the land of Egypt, we do not know what has become of him' And I said to them, 'Let any who have gold take it off'; so they gave it to me, and I threw it into the fire, and there came out this calf."* How is Aaron's explanation/excuse like what Adam and Eve do when God catches them in their sin (cf. Genesis 3: 8-13)?

Not my fault!

19. How do the Levites become the tribe consecrated to God's service?

Killing the idolators

AFTER THE FALL

20. Why was the Levitical priesthood necessary in the first place?

Nation not ready to be nation of priests

21. Give two reasons why the incident with the golden calf is like the Original Sin of Adam and Eve.

   a.

   b.

22. What does God hope to teach his people by laws of ritual purity?

23. Why does God impose a way of life upon his people that keeps them apart from the other nations?

24. Why does God demand animal sacrifices from the people?

25. What two functions do these laws serve for the people?

    a.

    b.

HEAVEN ON EARTH

26. What was the Tabernacle, and what purpose did it serve?

THE LAW

27. What does the name "Leviticus" mean?

28. What is the Book of Leviticus?

29. What is the reason behind all of the laws in the Book of Leviticus?

30. What incident from Leviticus shows the seriousness of God about being worshipped the way he wants to be worshipped?

31. Some of the foods forbidden to the Israelites are perfectly healthy to eat. We eat many of them to this day. Why does God forbid certain foods to be eaten?

32. What is unique about the form of government that would be formed through the laws and expressed in the Books of Exodus and Leviticus?

IN THE WILDERNESS

33. The book of the Bible that follows Leviticus is called _____ because . . .

     In Hebrew tradition it is called _____ because . . .

34. Explain why the people must wander in the wilderness for forty years.

35. What happens during the Israelite's journey in the desert that prevents Moses from entering into the Promised Land?

THE CONSTITUTION OF ISRAEL

36. What do the men of Israel do at Moab?

37. The name "Deuteronomy" means _____.

38. What is the difference between the laws laid down in Deuteronomy compared to those of Exodus and Leviticus?

39. How are the Books of Exodus and Leviticus like the Articles of Confederation from American History?

40. How is Deuteronomy like the United States Constitution?

41. What are two examples of concessions that Deuteronomy has to make to Israel's hard hearts?

    a.

    b.

42. What reality must Deuteronomy accept?

43. What is the prophetic aspect of Deuteronomy?

A CLOSE LOOK AT DEUTERONOMY

44. Who are the only three people who left Egypt and crossed the Red Sea who survive the forty years in the desert and arrive at the Jordan River?

   a.

   b.

   c.

45. Why, according to Moses, is the Second Law of the Book of Deuteronomy necessary?

46. What is repeated in Deuteronomy 5: 7-21?

47. The Great Shema is a prayer that every devout Jew knows by heart and prays several times a day. It is found in Deuteronomy 6: 4-5. Write it below.

48. How does this piece of our Jewish heritage live on in our Christian faith along with a key teaching from Leviticus 19: 18? (See Mark 12: 28-31)

VOCABULARY

Fill in the blanks with the appropriate words from the vocabulary section (text, p. 164).

49. Along with Moses, _____ and _____ were the only two of the first generation of Israelites who left Egypt to arrive at the banks of the Jordan River forty years later.

50. In the Bible, the word "lord" in all small letters would simply be a description of someone of some importance. "Lord" with a capital "L" would refer to a specific person. But when we see it written as "Lord" in all capital letters, we know that in the original Hebrew text, we would find _____.

51. "These are your gods, O Israel, who brought you up out of the land of Egypt!" was a blasphemy against God attributing his great deeds of power to _____.

52. _____ are a group of men in service to God who received their teaching and instruction from the Book of _____ whose name means "having to do with the _____".

53. From the Greek term "second law," the Book of _____ contains the laws that became a _____ for the Israelites.

54. Along with divorce, _____ was an evil consequence of Israel's lack of faith.

Name _____

Date _____

Hour _____

Chapter 9: The Rise of the Kingdom

1. What was God's ideal plan for the governance of Israel?

2. Due to their constant sin of idolatry, how did Israel end up being governed?

THE CONQUEST BEGINS

3. How old was Moses when he died?

    120

4. _____Josh_____ was Moses' successor.

5. Why did the Israelites never succeed in fully driving the Canaanites out of the Promised Land, and what was the long-term effect of this failure?
    Cananites were civilized / tempted by idolatry

6. After the Israelites crossed the Jordan River (which is a type of __baptism__), the first city they conquered was __Jordan__.

7. _____*Rahab*_____ was a woman who helped the spies Joshua sent across the Jordan River to gather information about the Promised Land.

8. What does St. Matthew (1: 5) tell us about this woman?

    Progenitor of David.

9. Describe how the Israelites conquered Jericho (cf. Joshua 6).

    God,

JOSHUA'S COVENANT WITH ISRAEL

10. We usually think of jealousy as a character fault. Yet God claims this trait for himself on several occasions when he gives Moses the First Commandment, he says,

    "'I am the LORD your God, who brought you out of the land of Egypt, out of the house of bondage. You shall have no other gods before me. You shall not make for yourself a graven image, or any likeness of anything that is in heaven above, or that is in the earth beneath, or that is in the water under the earth; you shall not bow down to them or serve them; **for I the LORD your God am a jealous God** [emphasis added], visiting the iniquity of the fathers upon the children to the third and the fourth generation of those who hate me, but showing steadfast love to thousands of those who love me and keep my commandments.'"

    Joshua warns the people that God is a jealous God (Joshua 24: 19-20). Before this, he challenges the people: "And if you be unwilling to serve the LORD, choose this day whom you will serve, whether the gods your fathers served in the region beyond the River, or the gods of the Amorites in whose land you dwell; but as for me and my house, we will serve the LORD" (24: 15).

    In the Book of Revelation (3: 15-16), Jesus warns the Christian community in Laodecia.

    "I know your works: you are neither cold nor hot. Would that you were cold or hot! So, because you are lukewarm, and neither cold nor hot, I will spew you out of my mouth."

    What does it mean when God says he is a jealous God?

    He will not countenance dalliance w/ other Gods. He alone deserves

    How do we provoke God's jealousy? What are some examples?

? Jealousy as admirable?

11. During this time of their history, how long did the people remain faithful to God?

As long as judges lived // until Josu's Tribal leaders Died.

THE RIGHT TIME TO ATTACK

12. God had vowed to give the Promised Land to Abraham's descendants. What was happening in the land of Canaan that facilitated its being conquered by the Israelites?

Civil wars

THE JUDGES

13. Judges 2: 11-23 gives us a pattern of how the events of the entire book will unfold. What is it?

Israel betrays, Judge rescues Israel repents

14. Why did Israel so easily abandon the covenant?

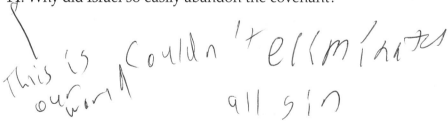

This is our world Couldn't elliminates all sin

15. What were some of the things that distinguished the Canaanites from the Israelites? Why did the Israelites admire the Canaanites?

Cities, rituals

SAMUEL THE KING-MAKER

16. Samuel was the last of the _____*Judges*_____.

17. The last verse in the Book of Judges is, *"In those days there was no king in Israel; every man did what was right in his own eyes."* The First Book of Samuel opens with Israel in a state of complete disarray. Samuel himself is a good man and does much to restore order in Israel. But as things began to unravel in his old age, what did the people demand of him?

King

18. How did Samuel react to this demand?

Why?

19. How did God reassure Samuel (1 Samuel 8: 7-9)?

It's not you, it's them

20. Samuel warned the people of the consequences of their demand (1 Samuel 8: 10-20). In three words, what would happen to the people if Samuel gave in to their demands?

a. *Oppression*

b. *taxes*

c. *war*

21. We can see that the people were rejecting the idea of being "a people set apart." If they were to accept God on his terms, what would God require of them, and how much would it cost them?

SAUL, THE ANOINTED ONE

22. Describe Saul's family background and physical appearance (1 Samuel 9: 1-2).

23. What does it mean to "anoint" something or someone?

24. The "anointed one" is rendered _____ in Hebrew and _____ in Greek.

25. What important fact was shown to the Israelites when their king was anointed by Samuel, the man of God?

SAUL'S FIRST BIG MISTAKE

26. Explain Saul's first big mistake.

27. What was the result of this mistake?

SAUL'S SECOND BIG MISTAKE

28. What was Saul's second big mistake?

29. What excuse did Saul offer Samuel for the sin he has committed?

30. How was Saul missing the point? What did God want from him?

31. For Saul's first offense he lost his _____, and for his second offense he lost his

_____.

THE MAN AFTER GOD'S OWN HEART

32. What mistake did God not want Samuel to make in anointing a successor to Saul?

33. What did God's spirit do regarding Saul and David?

34. The text describes an "ironic twist" to the story of Saul and David. What is it, and how is it like what happened with Moses (cf. ch. 7, #7)?

VOCABULARY

Using the vocabulary list for this chapter (text, p. 186), find each term in the grid below.

```
H  P  R  Q  L  D  N  N  T  M  P  A  L  E  S  T  I  N  E  D  M  V
A  V  C  H  R  I  S  T  F  K  G  L  J  Q  P  J  Y  P  C  B  P  D
Q  G  O  V  H  V  A  V  V  L  L  F  H  J  U  D  G  E  S  G  W  E
A  H  I  C  N  A  P  C  B  P  K  D  G  O  E  F  N  I  Z  T  Z  H
S  N  U  X  H  D  L  H  G  W  I  S  G  R  E  R  P  Q  G  O  G  W
S  G  U  V  L  D  V  H  I  A  V  A  V  D  G  Y  I  M  B  F  K  G
Z  H  J  B  R  D  C  N  Y  L  C  Q  G  A  V  H  T  C  V  V  L  L
X  J  M  G  W  A  X  H  H  L  I  A  H  N  C  N  Y  P  H  B  P  K
C  K  S  T  Z  H  H  J  A  I  Z  S  R  D  S  Y  S  J  H  O  D  W
V  L  A  S  S  G  W  A  M  B  A  Y  T  E  A  T  W  K  Y  T  E  Y
B  M  M  W  D  H  Q  L  B  J  Q  T  M  I  P  R  Q  L  T  M  H  T
S  A  U  L  R  D  A  P  E  A  P  H  H  L  N  V  P  B  F  A  G  R
M  B  E  Y  T  E  X  H  N  I  Z  L  S  V  H  E  O  V  V  N  L  J
A  V  L  T  M  E  S  S  I  A  H  P  D  C  N  H  S  C  B  T  K  H
P  C  B  F  K  G  W  K  J  J  Q  W  E  X  H  N  U  X  G  L  I  G
Z  O  A  H  I  L  Q  L  A  V  P  Z  H  S  J  S  Y  H  T  E  V  G
H  S  S  G  W  K  A  P  Q  G  O  S  G  W  K  A  T  N  Y  P  C  V
```

Name _____

Date _____

Hour _____

Chapter 10: The Kingdom of David

1. In Hebrew, "Ish" means "man." So what does the name "Ish-bosheth" mean?

   man of shame

2. Why did the writer change Ishbaal's name to Ishbosheth?

   No Baal reference

3. When Ishbaal's generals assassinated him, and brought his head to David, how did David deal with them?

   as traitors & murderers

4. In addition to David's actions regarding Ishbaal's assassins (cf. 2 Samuel 4: 1-12), review 1 Samuel 24: 1-22, 26: 1-25 and 2 Samuel 1: 1-16. How were David's behavior and character consistent in all of these episodes from his life?

   Mercy toward enemies
   love those who have both

JERUSALEM, DAVID'S NEW CAPITAL

5. Jerusalem was on the border between the land of _____*Judah*_____ and the land of _____*Israel*_____.

6. Why did David decide upon Jerusalem as his capital city?

Unite isreal
avoid charges
of favoritism

7. Up until the time that David took over the city of Jerusalem, why had it not been occupied by the Israelites?

Residents
had not been
defeated

8. The people who occupied Jerusalem before David conquered it were called _____.

9. _____Joab_____ was one of of David's generals who led the conquest of Jerusalem.

10. Jerusalem came to be known as CITY of David.

11. Who was King Hiram?

Phonecian king who
built Solomons
Temple

DAVID'S KINGDOM

12. The Temple was built three times. How were the three temples named?

   a. Sol 1

   b. Sol II

   c. Herod

BRINGING THE ARK TO JERUSALEM

13. What effect did bringing the Ark of the Covenant have on Jerusalem?

Holy²

14. What happened when David tried to bring the Ark to Jerusalem, and why?

15. When Saul tried to assume the role of a priest, he was punished by God. Why was David not punished when he assumed the role of priest as he brought the Ark of the Covenant to Jerusalem?

16. Why did David's wife Michal sneer and disapprove of David's dancing and merry-making before the Ark of God?

THE COVENANT WITH DAVID

17. What was the dilemma facing David, and what did he propose to resolve it?

18. At first, the prophet Nathan told David to go ahead, but that night God appeared to Nathan with another plan. What was it (cf. 2 Samuel 7: 4-17)?

BEYOND SINAI TO ZION

19. Fill in the following boxes that compare the Sinai Covenant to the Zion Covenant (with David).

THE SINAI COVENANT	THE ZION COVENANT
	Temple: A permanent structure to draw all people to Jerusalem.
National: The Sinai Covenant is with Israel only.	
	Inclusive: The Zion Covenant invites other nations in.
Torah: Law designed to keep Israel separate from other nations.	
	Todah: The thank offering is the most important religious ceremony.

THE DAVIDIC COVENANT: SEVEN PRIMARY FEATURES

20. God is offering David quite a lot. What are the parts of God's covenant with David?

a.

b.

c.

d.

e.

f.

g.

21. What is the difference between a nation and a kingdom?

22. How would God keep David's dynasty going?

23. How did Mt. Zion in Jerusalem eclipse Mt. Sinai?

24. What further meaning did Mt. Zion take on in the New Testament?

25. How did the existence of the Temple illustrate the universality of the Davidic Covenant?

THE DAVIDIC COVENANT: THREE SECONDARY FEATURES

26. List the three secondary features of the Davidic Covenant, and the New Testament figures to which they point.

SECONDARY FEATURE OF THE DAVIDIC COVENANT	NEW TESTAMENT FIGURE

VOCABULARY

Study the vocabulary terms on page 205. These may appear on your chapter quiz.

Name _____

Date _____

Hour _____

Chapter 11: Wise King Solomon

1. When God appeared to Solomon in a dream and asked him what he wants, how did Solomon respond, and why?

IMPERIAL ISRAEL

2. We read in 1 Kings 4: 20-21: *"Judah and Israel were as many as the sand by the sea; they ate and drank and were happy. Solomon ruled over all the kingdoms from the Euphrates to the land of the Philistines and to the border of Egypt; they brought tribute and served Solomon all the days of his life."* It may help to review Genesis 22: 17. To what did the sacred author refer to when he described the Israelites as being "as many as the sand by the sea"?

3. What unique arrangement took place between Israel and Egypt?

4. What does it mean when we read in the Bible (1 Kings 11: 3) that Solomon had 700 wives and 300 concubines?

5. We have been reminded a number of times in the textbook that polygamy usually brings problems. What happened to Solomon as a result of the relationships he had with so many women?

6. Why did the Queen of Sheba most likely visit Solomon?

THE WISDOM OF SOLOMON

7. How were some of the Primary Features of the Davidic Covenant (cf. chapter 10) illustrated by the visit of the Queen of Sheba to King Solomon?

8. What was the ultimate purpose of the Davidic Kingdom?

9. Why is it not a bad thing that parts of the Bible's wisdom literature actually came from pagan sources like Egypt or Babylon?

SOLOMON BUILDS THE TEMPLE

10. How had David prepared for the building of the Temple?

11. Why did Solomon have to import the talent necessary to build the temple, and from where did he import it?

12. How did the imported labor for the Temple fit into the aspects of the Davidic covenant that we studied in Chapter 10?

13. What are two traditions surrounding the building site of the Temple?

BUILDING MATERIALS FOR SOLOMON'S TEMPLE

14. What were the two primary building materials for Solomon's Temple, and where did they come from?

SOLOMON'S PRIDE AND APOSTASY

15. Name two of the great prices that the Israelites were paying for Solomon's glory.

    a.

    b.

16. List some of the ways that Solomon violated Moses' teachings from the Book of Deuteronomy.

17. Why do Solomon's wives turn out to be his most unbearable burden?

VOCABULARY

Study the vocabulary word list for this chapter (text, p. 219). With your book closed, unscramble the following words.

1. LENTEGI

2. NAAPG

3. BENESAEQFOUH

4. MOLOSNO

5. ORTHSATHE

6. SOPATYAS

7. MELPTE

8. LEHSO

9. CLIMMO

Place the unscrambled words in the numbered grid below. Once completed, the word revealed in the shaded boxes will help you answer the next question.

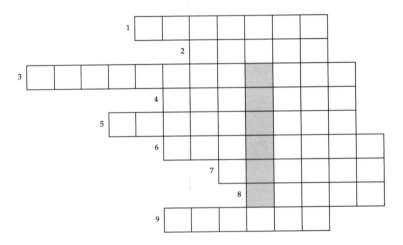

What was important to King Solomon, and how do we know this?

Chapter 12: The Divided Kingdom

1. What made Solomon unpopular with his subjects?

2. What were the seeds of the Israelite's undoing?

THE TORN KINGDOM

3. What did the prophet Abijah tell Jeroboam God was about to do, and how did he illustrate it?

4. What kind of a man was Solomon's son Rehoboam?

5. How did the elders counsel Rehoboam to deal with the people in the kingdom?

6. What did the younger men who had grown up with him counsel Rehoboam to do?

7. What was Rehoboam's final answer to those who came to him asking him to lighten the load?

8. What effect did Rehoboam's attitude and policies ultimately have on the kingdom?

9. With civil war looming, the kingdom divided with _____ in charge of

_____ in the south, and _____ ruling

_____ in the north.

BACK TO THE GOLDEN CALF

10. Why does Jeroboam bring back the Golden Calf (cf. 1 Kings 12: 26-28)?

GOOD KINGS AND BAD KINGS

11. How did the authors of the books of Kings and Chronicles define a bad king?

How did they define a good king?

12. Between Israel and Judah, who had more bad kings, and why?

13. Who were Jeroboam's golden calves supposed to represent?

14. What made the Canaanite gods and their cult so reprehensible?

15. During these confused times, who were God's spokesmen?

JONAH

The Book of the Prophet Jonah is only four chapters long and can be read in about twenty minutes. The student is encouraged to read this book before answering the following questions.

16. Where was Nineveh?

17. When God called Jonah to tell the people of Nineveh to repent, how did he respond, and why did he respond this way?

18. In running from God's call, where did Jonah try to go, and where was it?

19. While on the boat fleeing from God, a great storm came up, and Jonah confessed to his shipmates that he was the cause. They reluctantly dumped him overboard. What happened then?

20. How did the Ninevites respond to Jonah's call for them to repent?

21. Jonah had great success. The people of Israel had never reacted like this to the preaching of their prophets. How did Jonah react to his success?

22. What was God trying to teach Jonah by sending the leafy plant one day, and having the worm destroy it the next day?

23. When people think of the Book of the Prophet Jonah, what is the main image that comes to mind?

24. Yet what is the Book of the Prophet Jonah really about?

25. What were the difficulties of the life of a prophet illustrated in the Book of the Prophet Jonah?

26. How can we identify the false prophets of the Old Testament?

ELIJAH AND JEZEBEL

27. We saw earlier how Israel had more bad kings than did Judah. Who was the worst of the bad kings of Israel?

28. Who was King Ahab's wife, and what did she try to do?

29. Who was the prophet God sent to oppose the king and queen of Israel?

30. Describe how Elijah discredited the prophets of Baal.

ELIJAH AT SINAI

31. When Elijah fled for his life from Jezebel to Mt. Sinai, how did he encounter God?

32. What does this tell us we should do if we want to encounter God? What did Jesus do when he wanted to contact his father?

ELIJAH AND ELISHA

33. What two things did Elijah do that are similar to Moses' actions?

34. What was Elisha asking for when he asked Elijah for a "double share" of his spirit?

35. Why was it not presumptive or arrogant for Elisha to make this request?

THE ASSYRIAN THREAT

36. Name some things that the Assyrians did that made the kingdoms of Judah and Israel fear them.

THE END OF ISRAEL

37. How did King Hoshea, the last king of the northern kingdom of Israel, bring about the destruction of his kingdom by the Assyrians?

VOCABULARY

Study the vocabulary terms on page 236. With your book closed, complete the crossword puzzle.

ACROSS

2 An evil empire that terrorized the whole Middle East and constantly threatened Israel and Judah, eventually destroying Israel and scattering its people. (7)

3 Ahab's evil wife who worshipped Baal and persecuted God's prophets. (7)

7 The leader of the revolt against Rehoboam who became the first king of the northern kingdom of Israel. (8)

8 The northern center of worship of the Golden Calf in the northern kingdom of Israel. (3)

11 Elijah's successor who continued his mission in Israel. (6)

12 The worst of the evil kings of Israel. (4)

13 Jesus referred to the "sign of" this man as a type for his own death and resurrection. (5)

14 The southern center of worship in the northern kingdom of Israel that Jeroboam established for worshipping the Golden Calf. (6)

DOWN

1 The capital of the Assyrian Empire. (7)

3 The southern kingdom that kept Jerusalem as its capital and the successors of David as their kings. (5)

4 Solomon's son and heir whose arrogance caused the split of the northern and southern kingdoms. (8)

5 The prophet who announced to Jeroboam that God would give him ten of the twelve tribes of Israel. (6)

6 The far off place, perhaps in Spain, where Jonah planned to flee to escape his mission to Nineveh. (8)

9 The name of either the whole kingdom of the twelve tribes, or the northern of the two kingdoms that split after the death of King Solomon. (6)

10 The great prophet who challenged the pagan rulers of Israel and was taken up to heaven in a fiery chariot. (6)

Chapter 13: Conquest and Exile

CONQUEST AND EXILE

1. What brought the history of the northern kingdom of Israel to an end, and when does this happen?

2. How did the Assyrians deal with the people of Israel?

3. Which of the ten tribes were the only ones to survive, and where were they located?

4. How did the Assyrians ensure there would be no further trouble from the Israelites, and what people emerged from this strategy?

THE GREAT PROPHET ISAIAH

5. By this time, what was all that was left of David's kingdom?

6. While the Northern Kingdom of Israel was seeing its last days, who were the two men responsible for Judah undergoing a temporary rebirth?

7. During their days in the wilderness, the people had complained against God and Moses, and so to punish them God sent serpents into the camp to bite the people, and many died. When they cried out to Moses, God told him to make a bronze serpent and set it on a pole, and whoever looked at it would be healed (cf. Numbers 21: 4-9). What is the ultimate fate of this artifact from Israel's history (cf. 2 Kings 18: 4)?

8. How is the serpent on a pole still with us today?

9. What were some of the distinctive marks of Isaiah's preaching?

10. Who do most scholars believe wrote the Book of the Prophet Isaiah?

11. Isaiah correctly warned the people of the wrath that is to come if they did not repent. Why did the people have hope that God would never abandon them?

12. What does "There shall come forth a shoot from the stump of Jesse" mean? What is "the stump of Jesse"?

13. Isaiah tells us that the Spirit of the Lord shall rest upon the shoot that comes forth from Jesse's stump: "A spirit of wisdom and understanding, the spirit of counsel and might, the spirit of knowledge and fear of the Lord." Where have you heard or seen these words before?

14. Which is missing?

15. The lands of Zebulun and Naphtali were both merely shells of their former greatness. What was the land called that they now inhabited?

16. What did God promise them through Isaiah's prophecy?

17. Why did this prophecy of Isaiah seem so unlikely to come true?

18. What was the prophecy Isaiah gave to wicked King Ahaz?

19. What was the name of Ahaz's son, and why did he appear to be the one to fulfill Isaiah's prophecy?

20. To whom did Isaiah's prophecy really point?

THE WICKED KING MANASSEH

21. What were some of the crimes of King Manasseh?

22. What caused Manasseh to abandon his evil ways? What did he do after he repented?

THE GREAT REFORM

23. The Book of _____ was key to the reforms of King _____.

24. The great reformer King _____ was killed in battle by _____ of _____ in the year _____.

JEREMIAH SEES THE END OF THE WORLD

25. After the death of King Josiah, the Southern Kingdom of Judah was caught between the two great world powers of _____ and _____.

26. _____ was the leader of the Babylonian Empire.

27. What was the huge mistake King Zedekiah made?

28. Why was King Zedekiah's idea doomed to failure?

29. What demonstration did Jeremiah make to show the people the degree of destruction that was awaiting them?

THE IMPOSSIBLE PROMISE

30. What was the impossible promise?

31. During this whole era, the major sin of the people of Israel was _____.

32. The prophets often use the word _____ to describe Israel's unfaithfulness in worshipping other gods.

33. How is what you wrote in Question #32 illustrated in the life of the prophet Hosea?

34. Why did God send such terrible punishment upon his people?

35. Why would God redeem his people?

THE EXODUS REVERSED

36. When Nebuchadnezzar had had enough of rebellious Jerusalem, he came and destroyed it. When did this happen?

37. What was one of the things Jeremiah had done in preparation for the destruction of Jerusalem?

38. Where did Jeremiah end up, and how did this fulfill Moses' prophecy from Deuteronomy 28: 68?

THE BABYLONIAN EXILE

39. Often King David is credited for writing the Book of Psalms. How likely is it that King David wrote Psalm 137? Explain.

40. What good came out of the Israelites losing everything they held dear?

41. How did Jewish culture flourish during the time of the Exile?

42. Fill in the blanks below regarding the Major Prophets*: Isaiah, Jeremiah, and Ezekiel.

_____ went into exile in Babylon, and from there he heard of the total destruction of Jerusalem.

_____ prophesied the end of Jerusalem and encouraged the people to repent, but did not live to see his prophesies come true.

_____ demonstrated the destruction of Jerusalem by smashing a clay pot.

_____ and _____ both lived at the same time.

* *They are called the "Major Prophets" because their works are the longest prophetic works in the Bible. This title does not imply that the Minor Prophets (Amos, Joel, Hosea, Micah, etc.) are less important.*

DANIEL: HEROIC STORIES OF THE EXILE

43. While in exile in Babylon, why did Daniel and his companions eat only vegetables and drink only water?

44. Summarize the meaning of Nebuchadnezzar's dream that Daniel interpreted for him.

45. What did stories like Daniel interpreting Nebuchadnezzar's dream, Daniel in the lion's den, and the three young men Shadrach, Meshach, and Abednego (Hannaniah, Azariah, and Mishael) in the fiery furnace do for the exiled Jews?

VOCABULARY

Match the following words to their definitions. Then unscramble the letters in the shaded boxes to find the name that the Israelites gave to the bronze serpent they wickedly worshipped as a god before Hezekiah destroyed it.

_____ Babylon _____ Daniel _____ Messiah

_____ Exile _____ Naphtali _____ Galilee

_____ Remnant _____ Hezekiah _____ Isaiah

_____ Jeremiah _____ Nebuchadnezzar _____ Josiah

_____ Zebulun _____ Manasseh

J. The anointed one, or in Greek, "the Christ."

S. *"Land of Zebulun . . . Land of Naphtali . . . a people walking in darkness have seen a great light."* (Isaiah 9: 1-2).

T. A King whose reforms were based on the Book of Deuteronomy.

N. The great city where the Jews were taken into exile in 587 BC.

E. The great prophet who guided the reforms of Hezekiah and whose prophecies referred to the coming of the Messiah.

F. One northern tribe in Galilee not deported with the rest of Israel.

G. Another northern tribe in Galilee not deported with the rest of Israel.

W. The king of Babylon who exiled the best families of Jerusalem.

H. A king of Judah who started off evil, but later repented.

H. A great prophet who suffered many persecutions for speaking the truth.

A. One of the kings who temporarily reformed Judah to the pure worship of God.

U. The time that the Jews spent as captives in Babylon.

M. The small number of God's people who returned to Jerusalem after the Exile.

N. A great prophet who rose to prominence during the exile.

The pagan name given to Moses' bronze serpent is _____.
(If you need some help, look up 2 Kings 18: 4)

Chapter 14: A Remnant Returns

A REMNANT RETURNS

1. How long did Nebuchadnezzar's empire last after he died?

BELSHAZZAR'S FEAST

2. Why was Belshazzar's feast a sign of his incompetence and irresponsibility?

3. From where did the gold and silver goblets used at Belshazzar's feast come?

4. What remarkable thing happened during Belshazzar's feast?

5. How was Daniel drawn into this scene?

6. What did Daniel say the words meant?

CYRUS THE MESSIAH

7. What happened to Babylon soon after Belshazzar's feast?

8. How did the Persians differ from the Babylonians in their style of ruling the peoples they conquered?

9. What two great things did Cyrus of Persia do for the exiled Jews?

    a.

    b.

BEGINNING THE NEW JERUSALEM

10. How did most of the Jews respond to the news that they could return home?

11. From what two major deficiencies did the new Temple suffer?

    a.

    b.

TROUBLE WITH THE SAMARITANS

12. How did the Samaritans initially react to the Jews' project of rebuilding the Temple?

13. How did the Jews respond to the Samaritans at this point, and why?

14. Why did the project to rebuild the Temple get delayed?

15. After the death of Cyrus, King _____ searched the archives of Persia and found out that, indeed, King _____ had authorized the building of the temple, so he allowed the work to continue with the project being paid for by _____.

16. While the building of the Temple was delayed, what had the men of Jerusalem been doing?

17. Who were two of the prophets who spurred the men of Jerusalem to dedicate themselves again to the building of the Temple?

    a.

    b.

EZRA THE SCRIBE

18. What was Ezra's official position as a Jew?

19. What civil responsibilities did the Persian King entrust to Ezra?

20. What was the dilemma that faced Ezra as he tried to bring the people back to a pure worship of God?

21. As Ezra became the moral leader of the Jews, what were some of the things he did?

22. With Ezra as the spiritual leader of the people, _____ became the civil or political leader, who persuaded the Persian king to make him _____ of Jerusalem.

WHAT GOD REALLY WANTS

23. Many of the poor citizens of Jerusalem traded in their slavery in Babylon for what alternative?

24. The main religious problem in Jerusalem during the time of the Prophet Nehemiah was not

_____, but rather _____. This was manifested by what?

25. What was unacceptable about the sacrifices some people were making to God during this time?

26. In a word, what did God *really* want from his people?

THE PROMISE UNFULFILLED

27. What promise went unfulfilled at this time in history?

28. What was Judah called by the Persians?

VOCABULARY

29. The Babylonian empire, under the inept leadership of _____, fell very quickly to King _____ of _____. He allowed the Exiles to go home and promised to finance the rebuilding of their Temple in Jerusalem. The priest _____ led the Exiles back to Jerusalem and compiled a standard edition of the Old Testament Scriptures for them. At first the _____ had expressed an interest in helping rebuild the Temple, but the _____ refused to let them do so, because they worshiped pagan gods.

30. The new Temple was only a shadow of Solomon's Temple, and the _____ sat empty because the Ark of the Covenant had never been returned. Things were not the same as before. The people now spoke _____ instead of Hebrew. Jerusalem did not enjoy the prestige it had in previous days. _____ succeeded in rebuilding the city's defenses (i.e., the walls), but instead of the jewel that it had once been, Judah was known simply as _____ for the Persian province that contained it.

Name _____

Date _____

Hour _____

Chapter 15: Revolt of the Maccabees

REVOLT OF THE MACCABEES

1. Explain how the Jews and the Persians got along so well.

ONLY ONE WORLD TO CONQUER

2. What were some of the advances being made during this time in Greek culture?

3. During this period of history, Greece was a very loose confederation of city-states that were fiercely independent and often fought among themselves. Who brought them together?

4. Who conquered much of the known world of that time?

5. When we study history, what is the word that we use to describe Greek culture and civilization, and from where does it come?

JERUSALEM IN THE MIDDLE

6. How old was Alexander the Great when he died, and from what did he die?

7. What significant achievement was achieved concerning the Bible under Ptolemy II Philidelphus?

8. After Alexander's death, his kingdom was divided. The _____ ruled Egypt, the most famous and last of whom was Queen _____. The _____ ruled the old Persian Empire, with _____ caught in the middle.

9. One of the Seleucid kings, Antiochus IV referred to himself as "Epiphanes" which means _____, but his subjects referred to him as "Epimanes" meaning _____.

10. What were some of the abuses that were happening during the rule of Antiochus?

THE FINAL DESECRATION

11. Why did the Jews begin to call their religion "Judaism"?

12. What are some examples of the new persecution that broke out against the Jews under Antiochus?

AMAZING SUCCESS OF THE MACCABEES

13. The initial efforts of the Maccabees were unorganized and had little chance for success. Why, then, did people join the resistance?

14. Which of Matthias' sons was the most talented soldier?

15. By 125 BC, what had the Maccabees accomplished, and what still needed to be done if the prophecies were to be fulfilled?

WHAT THE JEWS BELIEVED

16. For the authors of the Books of the Maccabees, what did "Israel" mean?

17. What did some of the Jews at this time believe happened after death?

18. What were the people called who did not believe in the resurrection of the dead?

19. What is apostasy, and why would death be preferable to it?

20. Why do God's people suffer from time to time?

21. What important Christian doctrines are described in 2 Maccabees 12: 40-45 (reproduced in the textbook on page 282)?

JUDAS MACCABEUS AND THE STORY OF HANUKKAH

22. Most Christians are at least aware of the Jewish feast of Hanukkah because it is celebrated near the Christian feast of Christmas. What does Hanukkah celebrate?

VOCABULARY

Study the vocabulary words and definitions from this chapter. With your book closed, unscramble the following words. Place the unscrambled words in the boxes provided.

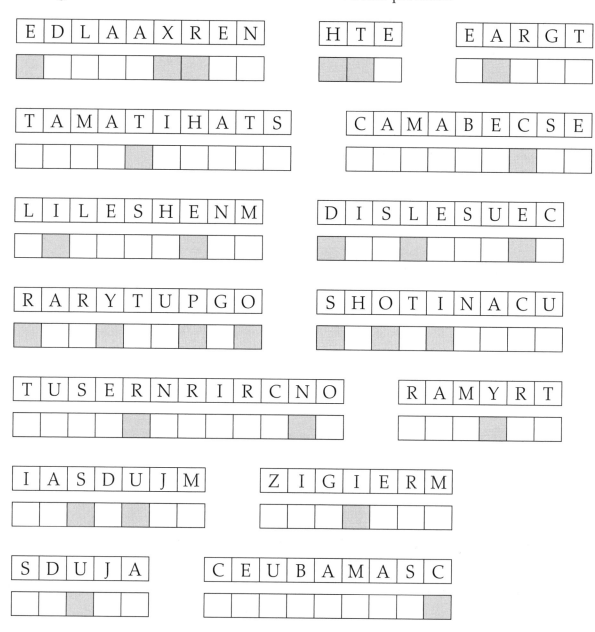

Now unscramble the letters from the shaded boxes to reveal the secret message.

— —   — —   — — —   —

— — —   W   — — —   — —

— — — —   F O —   — — — —   — — —

Name _____

Date _____

Hour _____

Chapter 16: The World of the New Testament

1. List four results of the Maccabean revolts that revealed the power of God to the Jews.

   a.

   b.

   c.

   d.

THE PROPHECIES FULFILLED?

2. How did John Hycranus purify the rest of the country of pagan influences?

3. What did John Hycranus do that caused problems with the Samaritans; problems that would last even through the time of Jesus?

4. John Hycranus did a remarkable job of restoring the territory of Israel. To many it looked like the prophecies of old were being fulfilled. What was the next step his successor, Aristobulus, took, and what was the problem with what he did?

5. After some time, the kingdom was once again divided between which two powerful factions?

   a.

   b.

THE PHARISEES

6. The word "Pharisee" comes from the Hebrew word "Perushim" which means

   _____.

7. Why was it understandable that the Pharisees would want to keep themselves separated from the pagans?

8. What were four things the Pharisees did to separate themselves from the rest of pagan society?

   a.

   b.

   c.

   d.

9. What is a phylactery?

THE SADDUCEES

10. List four distinctive beliefs of the Sadducees.

    a.

    b.

    c.

    d.

AFTER THE MACCABEES

11. What two factors worked against Israel maintaining its independence?

    a.

    b.

HEROD THE GREAT

12. What had Herod done that showed him to be insane?

13. What three factors contributed to the healthy economy of Herod's day?

    a.

    b.

    c.

14. When Herod the Great died in 4 BC, his kingdom was divided into four parts by the Romans and given to Herod's four sons. The divided kingdom was called the _____. The part that contained Galilee was ruled by _____ during the time of the ministry of Jesus.

WHEN THE TIME HAD FULLY COME

15. What were three of the benefits that the world enjoyed under the *Pax Romana*?

    a.

    b.

    c.

RELIGION IN THE ROMAN EMPIRE

16. Describe the Roman attitude toward religion.

17. What could the philosophers of the day deduce about God using only human reason?

18. How was the Roman religion impoverished and unable to provide for the spiritual needs of its believers?

THE SPREAD OF THE JEWISH RELIGION

19. What were the two cities of the ancient world with the greatest Jewish influence?

    a.

    b.

20. About _____ % of the population of the Roman Empire was Jewish.

21. What was the Septuagint?

(Note: In Biblical commentaries and other study tools about the Bible, the Septuagint is often abbreviated as "LXX" from the Roman numerals for "seventy.")

22. Why did the Jews begin to utilize synagogues?

23. How does the Jewish synagogue service still survive to this day in Christianity?

PROSELYTES OF THE GATE

24. Who were the "Proselytes of the Gate"?

25. Why were the "Proselytes of the Gate" such ready listeners and receivers of the early Christian message?

JUDEA AND GALILEE

26. What kind of trouble did Palestine cause for the Romans of the day?

27. The Israelites who inhabited Galilee were descendents of the tribes of _____ and

_____ .

THE SAMARITANS

28. Why did the Jews hate the Samaritans?

29. Where was Samaria located?

30. Why did the Samaritans believe that Mt. Gerizim was a more fitting place to worship God than Mt. Zion in Jerusalem?

31. What did the Samaritans have in common with the Sadducees?

32. Today, how many Samaritans survive?

VOCABULARY

Using the vocabulary list for this chapter (text, p. 302), find each term in the grid below.

```
A  V  P  G  Y  I  S  G  U  A  A  V  P  G  Y  G  M  B  F  K  G  L
Q  R  O  V  H  M  Z  H  J  Z  Q  G  O  V  H  T  A  V  V  L  L  F
A  H  I  C  N  H  E  R  O  D  T  H  E  G  R  E  A  T  B  P  K  D
S  N  U  S  H  R  C  K  N  F  S  N  U  X  H  H  L  E  G  P  I  S
D  S  Y  S  T  F  V  L  H  R  D  S  Y  S  J  N  I  T  T  H  U  A
E  A  T  W  K  O  B  M  G  A  L  I  L  E  E  M  K  R  S  A  J  Z
H  P  R  Q  L  B  B  N  T  M  H  P  R  Q  L  J  J  A  W  R  M  V
G  L  E  S  A  D  D  U  C  E  E  S  E  A  P  E  A  R  K  I  J  M
H  K  W  Z  O  T  A  V  L  L  S  N  U  X  H  N  I  C  T  S  H  P
J  J  Q  P  J  Y  P  C  B  U  D  S  Y  S  J  M  K  H  S  E  G  L
K  H  A  O  G  H  L  X  G  W  S  A  T  W  K  J  J  Y  W  E  H  K
L  J  O  H  N  H  Y  R  C  A  N  U  S  Q  L  A  V  P  G  S  J  J
P  F  D  K  D  M  K  A  S  S  G  L  E  A  P  Q  G  O  V  H  K  H
P  R  O  S  E  L  Y  T  E  S  O  F  T  H  E  G  A  T  E  N  L  G
```

Name _____

Date _____

Hour _____

Chapter 17: The New Testament

THE NEW TESTAMENT

1. The New Testament does not _____ the Old Testament. Rather it
   _____ the Old Testament.

2. St. Augustine says that the New Testament is _____ in the Old, and that the
   Old Testament is _____ in the New.

3. St. Irenaeus states, "The Law is pedagogy and prophecy of things to come." What do we mean by "the Law" when the "L" is capitalized?

   What does it mean that the Law is a pedagogy (cf. Galatians 3: 23-26)?

HOW THE NEW TESTAMENT IS ORGANIZED

4. The books of the New Testament can be put into the same classes as those of the Old Testament. Write a few examples of each.

OLD TESTAMENT BOOKS	CLASSIFICATION	NEW TESTAMENT BOOKS
	Law	
	History	
	Wisdom	
	Prophecy	

THE NEW LAW: THE FOUR GOSPELS

5. If all of the Gospels tell the same story, why are there so many differences between them?

6. The Gospels of Sts. _____, _____, and _____ are

called the _____ Gospels, from a Greek word that means _____.

This is because compared to the Gospel of St. _____, which is quite different

from them, they share a similar point of view.

7. While there is no definitive proof, most scholars agree Sts. _____ and _____ probably used a copy of St. _____'s Gospel as a kind of outline for their own Gospels. Scholars further theorize that they may have also used another source called _____ that might have been a compilation of the sayings of Jesus.

8. The differences we find in the Gospels _____ the truth of what they are telling us. They do not _____ the truth.

MATTHEW

9. For whom did St. Matthew primarily write his Gospel?

10. St. Matthew was also known as _____ and used to work as a _____.

11. What did St. Matthew emphasize about Jesus in his Gospel?

MARK

12. For whom did St. Mark primarily write his Gospel?

13. Where did St. Mark get most of his information about Jesus for his Gospel?

14. St. Mark sees Jesus as a new Moses leading the people on a new Exodus. What about Jesus' ministry does St. Mark mostly emphasize?

15. Explain the odd little story that we find only in St. Mark's Gospel. What do most scholars think it means?

LUKE

16. For whom did St. Luke primarily write his Gospel?

17. We know from St. Paul's writings that St. Luke practiced what profession?

18. In addition to the Gospel that bears his name, what other book of the New Testament did St. Luke write?

19. In the years following Jesus' work on earth, many things were written about him. There are, for example, Gospels of Sts. Peter, Thomas, and James, to name a few. Give two reasons why St. Luke wrote another gospel.

    a.

    b.

20. From where do many believe that St. Luke got this information?

JOHN

21. For whom did St. John primarily write his Gospel?

22. Why do many scholars believe St. John wrote his gospel for this audience (your answer to Question #21)?

23. What phrase did St. John use to describe himself in his Gospel?

24. While he did not go into a lot of theological depth in explaining it, which doctrine of God's existence does St. John most completely reveal to us?

HISTORY: THE ACTS OF THE APOSTLES

25. How has the historical truth of St. Luke's Gospel been verified over the years?

26. From reading the Acts of the Apostles, how do we know that St. Luke was an eyewitness to much of what he wrote?

WISDOM: THE EPISTLES

27. Why did Sts. Peter, Paul, and John write their letters?

28. In general, all of the letters of the New Testament are written either to _____ or to _____.

29. What was the purpose of St. Paul's brief letter to Philemon?

30. Who wrote the Letter to the Hebrews, and what is its primary teaching?

PROPHECY: THE REVELATION

31. The images and symbols used in the Book of Revelation can make it hard to understand. What is the main point of this book?

VOCABULARY

_____ From the Latin word *evangelium* which means "Good News."

_____ As with many details of Jesus' early life, this is found only in the Gospel of St. Luke.

_____ This word is used to describe the Gospels of Sts. Matthew, Mark, and Luke, since they have a similar point of view of Jesus' life, especially when compared with the Gospel of St. John.

_____ A series of Jesus' sayings that are attributed to this hypothetical source.

_____ These Epistles were written for the whole Church.

_____ St. Paul says that the Law of Moses fulfilled this role for us until we were ready for true Freedom in Christ.

_____ The Greek word for a letter, as in correspondence written from one person to another.

_____ Used to describe Jesus' most intimate friends and followers as well as St. Paul.

Chapter 18: The Incarnation

1. The word *incarnation* comes from Latin and means _____.

2. Having read the parts of the Gospels of Sts. Matthew, Luke, and John, as directed on page 320 of the text, read also the first chapter of St. Matthew and Mark 1: 1-20, then fill in the following grid.

GOSPEL	WHEN WRITTEN (CIRCA)	AT WHAT POINT IN JESUS' LIFE DO WE KNOW THAT HE IS GOD?	GENEALOGY? (YES/NO) IF YES, HOW FAR BACK?
Mark	AD 65		
Matthew	AD 70-75		
Luke	AD 80-85		
John	AD 90-100		

As the Church wrestled with the idea of the Incarnation—of God becoming man—what happened to her awareness of the Divinity of Jesus as time went on as evidenced by the Gospels?

3. All religions have moral codes and beliefs. What is the distinctive belief of Christianity that no other religion shares?

THE SON OF DAVID

4. The family tree of Jesus in St. Matthew's Gospel goes back to Abraham. How does St. Matthew subtly connect Jesus to Adam?

5. If we were to compare St. Matthew's genealogy carefully to the historical books of the Old Testament, the lists of names would not match up precisely. Why?

6. In Matthew 1: 17 the family tree of Jesus is divided into how many important events from Israel's history?

7. Biblically speaking, what does this number mean?

8. How many generations does St. Matthew include in each section of his geneology?

9. List two reasons why this number is deeply symbolic.

    a.

    b.

10. List the three important events that sum up Israel's history for St. Matthew:

    a.

    b.

    c.

11. This history seems to end on a sad but hopeful note with St. Matthew. What is his Good News?

HAIL MARY

12. Only _____ gives us the story of the Archangel Gabriel coming to Mary to announce that she had been chosen by God to be the mother of Jesus. He probably got this information from _____.

13. What is the difference between a betrothal in the time of Jesus and an engagement in our own time?

14. In the Litany of the Blessed Virgin Mary, there are many titles given to Mary. Why is she also given the title "Ark of the Covenant"?

15. Look up the following episodes from the Old Testament.

   • How does the first couple respond to God's will (Genesis 3: 1-7, especially vv. 6)?

   • How does Moses respond to God's will (Exodus 3 and 4, especially 3: 11-13 and 4: 1, 4: 10-13)?

   • How does Jeremiah respond to God's will (Jeremiah 1: 6-7)?

   • How does Jonah respond to the will of God (Jonah 1: 1-3)?

- How does Mary respond to God's will (Luke 1: 38)?

- How do you think the first readers of St. Luke's Gospel would have reacted to Mary's response to God's request of her?

16. Pope Bl. Pius IX declared the dogma of the Immaculate Conception to be an infallible element of the Catholic Faith.

   - What does the dogma of the Immaculate Conception teach?

   - What is the Scriptural basis for this belief?

THE BIRTH OF JESUS

17. St. Luke describes the historical setting of Jesus' birth by what historical events?

   a.

   b.

   c.

18. Why does it not matter that modern historians have had a hard time pointing exactly to when all of these events took place?

19. Jesus is born in David's hometown of Bethlehem. The name of the town is a compound Hebrew word:

Beth = House   Lehem = Bread

So the name of the town where Jesus was born means _____.

    Look at John 6: 51-52:

    "I am the living bread which came down from heaven; if anyone eats of this bread, he will live for ever; and the bread which I shall give for the life of the world is my flesh."

Luke 2: 7 says that Mary placed Jesus in a manger which is a _____.

20. Only St. Luke tells us about the angels visiting the shepherds. They are told that "to you is born this day in the city of David a (a)Savior, who is (b)Christ the (c)Lord" (Luke 2: 11). By using these titles, what would the shepherds have immediately known about Jesus:

    a.

    b.

    c.

21. How were shepherds regarded in Jesus' time?

NUNC DIMITTIS

22. Forty days after Christmas, we celebrate the Feast of the Presentation of Jesus in the temple. By what other name is this feast sometimes called, and why is it called this?

23. When Mary and Joseph bring Jesus to the temple they are greeted by two people. Who are they?

    a.

    b.

24. What does the Latin phrase *nunc dimittis* mean, and where does it come from?

25. Three canticles from the Gospel according to St. Luke are prayed daily in the Liturgy of the Hours. (These are often called by their first words in Latin.) The Canticle of Zechariah, prayed in the morning, is called *Benedictus* (Blessed be [*Benedictus*] the Lord God of Israel . . . ; Luke 1: 68-79). The Canticle of Mary, prayed in the evening, is called *Magnificat* (My soul magnifies [*magnificat*] the Lord . . . ; Luke 1: 46-55). The *Nunc dimittis* is prayed at night (Lord, now [*nunc*] lettest thou thy servant depart [*dimittis*] in peace . . . ; Luke 2: 29-32). Who originally spoke this third canticle?

26. Simeon prophesies to Mary that her own heart will be pierced by a sword as a foretelling of the grief that will await her as the Mother of the Savior. This is the beginning of an ancient Catholic piety called the Seven Sorrows of Mary. Look up the sources listed below and finish filling in the sorrows that are described.

SOURCE	SORROW OF MARY IT DESCRIBES
Luke 2: 35	Simeon's Prophecy
Matthew 2: 13-15	
Luke 2: 41-45	
The Fourth Station of the Cross	
John 19: 25	
John 19: 38-40	
John 19: 41-42	

THE EPIPHANY

27. According to the Gospel of St. Matthew, how many Wise Men are there (cf. Matthew 2: 1-12)?

28. Tradition most likely determines the number of Wise Men according to the gifts they brought. The gifts of gold, frankincense, and myrrh have a deep symbolic meaning. What do they mean?

Gold means Jesus is _____.

Frankincense means Jesus is _____.

Myrrh means Jesus is _____ and also points to his _____.

THE HOLY INNOCENTS

29. Why does Herod order the murder of all male children in and around Bethlehem who are two years of age and under?

30. How does the slaughter of the Holy Innocents make Jesus to be like Moses?

The feast of the Holy Innocents is celebrated on December 28. They have come to be celebrated as the patron saints of the innocent children murdered by the crime of abortion.

TEACHING THE TEACHERS

31. Why is it that St. Luke is the only Evangelist to record the story from Jesus' childhood of being "lost" in the temple?

32. What aspect of the Mystery of the Incarnation does this episode about Jesus when he was twelve years old illustrate for us?

VOCABULARY

Study the vocabulary terms on page 336. These may appear on your chapter quiz.

Name _____

Date _____

Hour _____

Chapter 19: What Jesus Did

WHAT JESUS DID

1. Why will we find differences in the flow of events of Jesus' life as they are reported to us in the Gospels?

JOHN THE BAPTIST MAKES STRAIGHT THE WAY

2. From which tribe of Israel did John the Baptist descend?

3. Why did the Gospel writers go to the trouble of describing what John the Baptist looked like and what he wore?

4. When John appeared telling people that the Kingdom of God is at hand, what did many of them think he meant by this?

5. In Chapter 2 (p. 38 of the text), we studied "typology." Some people thought that the prophecy found in Malachi 4: 5 meant that Elijah would come back from the dead. We are told, however, that Jesus interprets this "typologically." What does this mean?

JESUS BAPTIZED

6. John the Baptist pointed out that it should be Jesus baptizing John, not the other way around. But Jesus insisted, saying, "it is fitting to fulfill all righteousness." What did Jesus mean by that?

7. Remembering the tribe that John the Baptist descended from, why is it fitting that John would help Jesus inaugurate his mission by baptizing him?

THE TEMPTATION IN THE WILDERNESS

8. Jesus' fast of forty days in the desert is like (and perhaps even prefigured as a type) from what other similar events from the Old Testament?

   a.

   b.

   c.

   d.

9. Remember that for Jesus to be truly tempted, he would really have had to consider what the devil was proposing to him. With this in mind, why would Jesus be tempted to . . . .

   . . . turn stones into bread?

   . . . jump off the pinnacle of the temple?

   . . . worship the devil in exchange for political power?

10. Again, seeing the story typologically, we see Jesus as the new Adam who was able to overcome the sin to which Adam submitted. What was it?

11. What temptation did Jesus overcome in the desert that the Israelites gave into while they were in the desert?

WATER INTO WINE

12. What is St. John trying to teach us by including the story of the water changed into wine in the second chapter of his Gospel?

CLEANSING OF THE TEMPLE

13. Why were there money changers in the temple courtyard?

14. It would appear that the money changers were simply providing a necessary service. What was wrong with what they were doing?

15. Why were people selling animals in the temple courtyard?

16. Again, it would appear that those who were selling animals were providing a convenience and a service to those visiting the temple. What was the problem with what they were doing?

17. It is common in our day for people to give a priest money, for example, after he performs a wedding or Baptism, or after saying a funeral Mass. Isn't this the same thing?

THE LAND OF ZEBULUN AND NAPHTALI

18. The name of the town that Jesus had made his headquarters was _____. Where was it was located?

HEALING THE SICK

19. The Bible associates physical sickness with _____.

20. Other than the extraordinary nature of a miraculous healing, why did Jesus' healing miracles attract so much attention?

21. People were glad to receive Jesus' healings. What other power did he claim to have that those in authority did not want to accept?

WHO SINNED?

22. What is the ironic twist in the story about Jesus healing the two blind men (Matthew 9: 27-30)?

CASTING OUT DEMONS

23. Again, what is the irony in the stories of Jesus casting out demons?

EATING WITH SINNERS

24. Explain why tax collectors were so hated in the time of Jesus.

25. What reason does Jesus give for associating with outcasts and those known to be sinners?

WOMEN AND SAMARITANS

26. Why would Jesus reach out to the Samaritans?

27. Why were women so attracted to Jesus and his message?

THE TWELVE

28. What is the significance of Jesus selecting twelve of his disciples to be his apostles?

29. The word "apostle" comes from a Greek word that means _____.

30. Why did some of the apostles, like many Jews of their time, use two names?

HOSANNA TO THE SON OF DAVID

31. If indeed Jesus were to ride into his own capital city as a victorious king, we would expect him to be on a white horse or riding in a chariot. Why does he ride into Jerusalem on a donkey?

VOCABULARY

Study the vocabulary terms on page 360. With your book closed, complete the crossword puzzle.

ACROSS

2 The title given to Jesus as the perfect sacrifice who takes away the sins of the world. (9)
4 To wash ceremonially. (7)
6 One of the fallen angels who rebelled against God. (5)
7 Someone suffering from any number of, what were at the time of Jesus, incurable skin diseases. (5)
8 People who made their living by changing Roman currency for the coins of the Temple so that people could pay the Temple tax. (13)
10 The outer area of the temple where anyone could be. It is where Jesus cleared out the vendors and money changers. (18)
11 To go without food in order to derive a spiritual benefit. (4)
12 To test someone by offering them something that is forbidden. (5)

DOWN

1 The cousin of Jesus who prepared the world for his coming. (14)
3 A town on the northern shore of the Sea of Galilee that was Jesus' home during his ministry. (9)
5 Also the number of the Tribes of Israel, these were Jesus' closest friends whom he chose to help him with his ministry. (9)
9 Someone who makes a journey for religious reasons. (7)

Name _____

Date _____

Hour _____

Chapter 20: What Jesus Taught

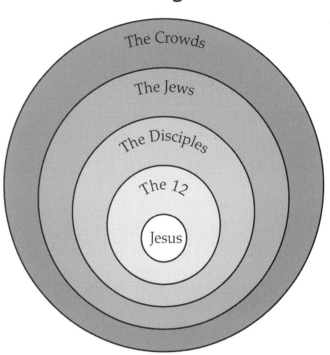

WHAT JESUS TAUGHT

1. Read John 6: 22-71 very carefully. It is called "The Bread of Life" discourse by Scripture scholars. In this discourse, there are four distinct groups of people that Jesus is dealing with: The Crowds, The Jews, The Disciples, and the Twelve. Notice that in verse 22, St. John is referring to the crowd, and Jesus deals with them until verse 40.

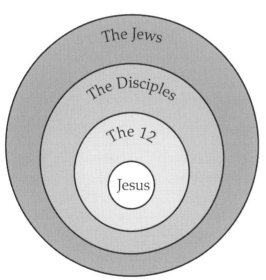

In verse 41, the attention shifts from "the crowd" to "the Jews." So when Jesus refers to himself as "the bread of life," what happened to "the crowds"?

2. In verses 41-59, Jesus is trying to convince "the Jews" of his thinking. What is the advantage Jesus would have with "the Jews" that he did not have with "the crowds"?

3. How do the Jews react to Jesus' teaching "I am the bread which came down from heaven" (v. 41)?

4. What does Jesus add in verses 50-51 to the teaching that he is the bread of life?

5. How do the Jews respond to this teaching?

6. It should be clear at this point, Jesus, having lost "the crowds," is now at the point of losing "the Jews" as well. What does he say in verses 53-59 that he did not say in verse 51?

7. In verses 60-66 the attention shifts from "the Jews" to "the disciples." What can we assume happened to "the Jews"?

8. Now Jesus is left with "the disciples" and "the twelve." What advantage would he have enjoyed with this smaller and more intimate group of friends and followers?

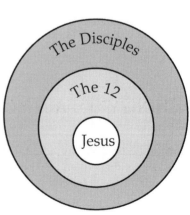

9. How do "the disciples" react to Jesus' teaching in verses 60 and 66?

10. Now Jesus is left with just whom?

11. How does Jesus reconcile the truth of what he is trying to teach with the fact the more he tries to explain it, the more of his audience leaves?

12. Having lost nearly everyone who had been listening to him, what does Jesus ask the Twelve in verse 67?

13. Based on this section of St. John's Gospel, what is Jesus himself teaching in regards to the nature of the Sacrament of the Eucharist? Is it a "symbol" or a "representation" of Jesus, or is it Jesus himself?

14. Based on Jesus' example, what should the Catholic Church do in regards to her constant teaching that the Eucharist really is the Body and Blood of Jesus under the forms of bread and wine?

TEACHING WITH AUTHORITY

15. The Bible reports that those who heard Jesus were impressed by the fact that he taught "with authority." What does this mean?

PARABLES

16. What is a parable?

17. Explain the point the text is making about parables when it uses the example of the parable of the people who built their houses on rock as opposed to sand.

THE KINGDOM OF GOD IS AT HAND

18. What are two of the ways that people should live in the Kingdom of God?

   a.

   b.

BORN FROM ABOVE

19. What is the significance of Nicodemus referring to Jesus as "Rabbi"?

20. What is Jesus talking about when he tells Nicodemus that we must be "...born anew...of water and the Spirit..."?

THE LETTER OF THE LAW IS NOT ENOUGH

21. Daniel's father asks him to clean out the garage. Daniel asks when his dad wants the work completed. His father tells him "sometime within the next day or so."

    If Daniel says to himself, "Well I guess that means I can put it off for a few days." He is obeying the _____ of the law in obeying his father. Explain your answer.

    If Daniel makes it a priority to have the garage cleaned out by the same time tomorrow, he is obeying the _____ of the law. Explain your answer.

22. From the standpoint of the letter of the law, why did it make sense for the priest and the Levite to pass by the man who had been beaten by the robbers?

THE LAST SHALL BE FIRST

23. Why did Jesus attract the poor and the outcast with his teachings?

THE FIRST SHALL BE LAST

24. Was Jesus teaching that only the poor and outcast would be able to go to heaven? What about the rich and the well-off?

LOVE YOUR ENEMIES

25. Aside from the fact that Jesus requires us to forgive those who offend or hurt us, why is it simply a reasonable thing to do?

26. When St. Peter asks Jesus if he must forgive seven times, he is using a biblical figure of speech. What does it mean?

27. When Jesus tells St. Peter he must forgive "seventy times seven" times, what does he mean?

GOD'S GRACE IS UNDESERVED

28. In the fifteenth chapter of St. Luke's Gospel, Jesus tells three parables. What are they?

    a.

    b.

    c.

29. To whom is Jesus directing these parables, and why?

30. St. Luke is describing a scene that includes Jesus, scribes, Pharisees, tax collectors, and sinners. To whom do they correspond in the parable of the Prodigal Son?

    a. Jesus

    _____

    b. scribes and Pharisees

    _____

    c. tax collectors and sinners

    _____

31. Since Jesus is directing the parable towards the scribes and the Pharisees, who is really the main character in the parable?

32. This parable is often used to illustrate the forgiveness of God. Considering who is the main character of the parable, what then is the point of the parable?

33. Why must we overcome the human desire for strict justice (i.e., according to the letter of the law)?

PRAY WITHOUT CEASING

34. What is the model prayer given to us by Jesus?

35. From this prayer, we get the essential parts of any prayer.

    (a) Addressing God

    (b) Praising God for his goodness

    (c) Acknowledging what God has accomplished in the past

    (d) Petitions (asking God for favors, forgiveness, grace, and mercy)

Label where you find these components in the Lord's Prayer.

(_____)Our Father, who art in heaven, (_____)hallowed be thy Name. (_____)Thy kingdom come, thy will be done, on earth as it is in heaven. (_____)Give us this day our daily bread, and forgive us our trespasses. As we forgive those who trespass against us. And lead us not into temptation, but deliver us from evil. Amen.

JESUS IS THE BREAD OF LIFE

36. In the first section of this chapter, we examined the Bread of Life discourse as an example of how Jesus taught with authority. Here we should review the biblical background for our belief in the Real Presence of Jesus in the Holy Sacrament of the Eucharist. We are already familiar with Jesus' forceful teaching from the Gospel of St. John.

"I am the bread of life." (John 6: 35)

"I am the living bread which came down from heaven; if any one eats of this bread, he will live for ever; and the bread which I shall give for the life of the world is my flesh." (John 6: 51)

"Truly, truly, I say to you, unless you eat the flesh of the Son of man and drink his blood, you have no life in you; he who eats my flesh and drinks my blood has eternal life, and I will raise him up at the last day. For my flesh is food indeed, and my blood is drink indeed. He who eats my flesh and drinks my blood abides in me, and I in him. As the living Father sent me, and I live because of the Father, so he who eats me will live because of me. This is the bread which came down from heaven, not such as the fathers ate and died; he who eats this bread will live for ever." (John 6:53-58)

The tradition of the Last Supper in the Synoptic Gospels is passed on to us very clearly in the Gospel of St. Mark.

"And as they were eating, he took bread, and blessed, and broke it, and gave it to them, and said, 'Take; this is my body.' And he took a cup, and when he had given thanks he gave it to them, and they all drank of it. And he said to them, 'This is my blood of the covenant, which is poured out for many.'" (Mark 14: 22-24)

We find a consistent teaching in the writings of St. Paul.

"For I received from the Lord what I also delivered to you, that the Lord Jesus on the night when he was betrayed took bread, and when he had given thanks, he broke it, and said, 'This is my body which is for you. Do this in remembrance of me.' In the same way also the cup, after supper, saying, 'This cup is the new covenant in my blood. Do this, as often as you drink it, in remembrance of me.' For as often as you eat this bread and drink the cup, you proclaim the Lord's death until he comes. Whoever, therefore, eats the bread or drinks the cup of the Lord in an unworthy manner will be guilty of profaning the body and blood of the Lord. Let a man examine himself, and so eat of the bread and drink of the cup. For any one who eats and drinks without discerning the body eats and drinks judgment upon himself." (1 Corinthians 11: 23-29)

Review these Scripture passages carefully. Note well how both Jesus and St. Paul make plentiful use of the verb "to be" as they reiterate phrases such as "I *am* the bread of life." "My flesh *is* true food and my blood *is* true drink." "This *is* my body; this *is* my blood."

St. Paul makes the case perfectly clear when he teaches us that receiving the Eucharist in the state of mortal sin makes us answerable for Jesus' body and blood.

Is there anything in any of these biblical teachings on the Eucharist that indicates that after the consecration the bread and wine are mere symbols or representations of Jesus? Does Jesus or St. Paul anywhere say "this *represents* my body; this *symbolizes* my blood?!?"

VOCABULARY

Study the vocabulary words and definitions from this chapter. With your book closed, unscramble the following words. Place the unscrambled words in the boxes provided.

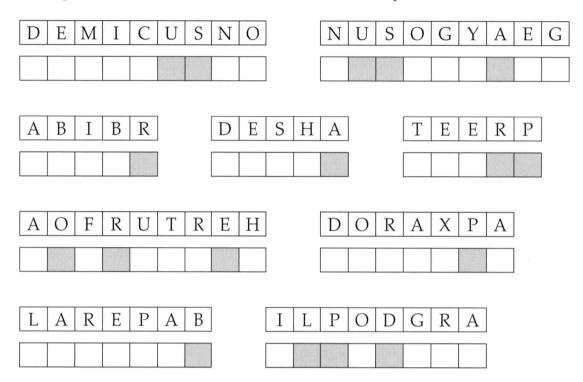

Now unscramble the letters from the shaded boxes to reveal a key teaching of Jesus.

— — — — — V̲ —

— — — —   — — — — — —

Name _____

Date _____

Hour _____

Chapter 21: The Cup of Consummation

THE CUP OF CONSUMMATION

1. What is the definition of the noun "consummation"?

2. The Passover of the Jews celebrates the Angel of Death "passing over" the faithful Hebrew people who had marked their door posts and lintels with the blood of the paschal lamb (cf. Exodus 12: 13). How does Jesus, the perfect Passover Lamb, bring to fulfillment this ancient ritual?

THE MISSING CUP

3. Imagine a child's birthday party. After all the children have arrived the festivities generally begin with some games, followed by the birthday cake, and then opening of the gifts. How do you think most people would react if one of these were skipped or dropped out of the party?

4. Describe what happens at a Passover supper as each cup of wine is poured and shared:

    a.

    b.

    c.

    d.

5. How did Jesus change some of the elements of the Passover meal at the Last Supper?

    a.

    b.

    c.

6. The Last Supper is the first Mass. Which two sacraments did Jesus institute at this time?

    a.

    b.

7. At this point, who is the only apostle not with Jesus and the other apostles (that is, who was the first person to leave Mass early)?

IN GETHSEMANE

8. The word "Gethsemane" means _____.

9. We have seen earlier that numbers have symbolic meanings in the Bible. What does the number three mean when used in the Bible?

10. Jesus tells St. Peter that ". . . before the cock crows twice, you will deny me three times." Paraphrase this. What was Jesus telling St. Peter?

11. Which of the apostles does Jesus take with him into the garden to keep watch with him while he prays?

12. Aside from other miracles and great acts of Jesus, what other key event in Jesus' life had these men witnessed?

13. In the Garden of Gethsemane, Jesus prays, *"Abba, Father, all things are possible to thee; remove this cup from me; yet not what I will , but what thou wilt."* What are the two meanings given to this cup from the text and the excerpt from the *Catechism of the Catholic Church*?

    a.

    b.

14. Why would the apostles have had a hard time staying awake with Jesus while he prayed?

JESUS ARRESTED IN GETHSEMANE

15. What was the purpose behind Judas greeting Jesus with a kiss?

16. What was Jesus' last miracle before his death?

EXTRA FOR EXPERTS

The story of the ear of the high priest's slave being cut off appears in all four Gospels. But, as we saw back in Chapter 17, the details of this story vary from Gospel to Gospel. With this in mind, get out your Bible and find the following answers (Matthew 26: 47-56, Mark 14: 43-52, Luke 22: 47-53, John 18: 2-12).

- Jesus only heals the man's ear in the Gospel of St. _____.

- St. Peter is identified as the one who cut off the high priest's slave's ear only in the

  Gospel of St. _____.

- The name of the high priest's slave is _____, and this detail

  is given to us only by St. _____.

17. Who were the two apostles that followed Jesus after he was arrested?

    a.

    b.

18. Annas was the legitimate high priest at the time Jesus was arrested. Why did he defer to Caiaphas in allowing him to interrogate Jesus first?

PETER'S DENIAL

19. How was St. Peter identified as a follower of Jesus?

20. What is the crucial difference between St. Peter's denial of Jesus and that of Judas?

BLASPHEMY!

21. Why would the Sanhedrin have convened in the middle of the night to hear Jesus' case?

22. The Gospels say that some people came forth and gave false testimony against Jesus. According to the Law of Moses, the testimony of two or three witnesses was sufficient to convict a person of a crime. Why was the testimony of those who witnessed against Jesus not sufficient to condemn him?

23. How is Jesus finally convicted of blasphemy?

24. What does the gesture of a Jew tearing his clothes mean, and what was particularly remarkable about the high priest tearing his robes?

25. Now that they had their conviction of a crime that warranted death as Moses taught, why did the Jewish authorities not carry it out?

26. _____ would have the final word over Jesus' fate.

JUDAS REPENTS

27. Judas realizes once it is too late that things have not turned out the way that he had planned. When he realized the Jewish leadership was planning to kill Jesus, he tried to undo what he had done. How do the chief priests and elders respond when Judas comes back offering to give back the money?

28. When Judas throws the thirty pieces of silver back at them, what do they do with the money?

29. According to St. Matthew (27: 5), how does Judas meet his demise?

What does St. Luke, in the Acts of the Apostles (1: 15-19), report?

PILATE EXAMINES JESUS

30. The crime of blasphemy would not matter to Pilate under Roman law. The Jewish leadership no doubt knew this, so what do they accuse Jesus of in front of Pilate?

31. How does Pilate initially respond to the demands of the Jewish leadership that Jesus be put to death?

CRUCIFY HIM!

32. When Jesus' opponents insist that Pilate do something, he sends Jesus to Herod Antipas, the governor of Galilee. How does this turn out (cf. Luke 23: 6-12)?

33. What is the bitter irony of the convict with the name "Barabbas," who the crowd demanded be released instead of Jesus?

34. Pilate has Jesus scourged. What two things does he hope to accomplish by this?

      a.

      b.

35. In the end, why does Pilate cave in to the demands of the mob?

36. What is the official teaching of the Catholic Church regarding the Jews and culpability for the death of Jesus?

JESUS CRUCIFIED

37. What is the name of the man whom the Romans pressed into service to help carry Jesus' cross, and by what right did they do this?

38. Why did they offer Jesus wine to drink that was mixed with myrrh?

39. St. John tells us about the inscription above Jesus' head. In our day, many crucifixes have the letters "INRI" on them.

  • What do these letters mean?

  • Why would the Jewish leaders come back to Pilate and ask him to change the inscription (John 19: 21)?

  • What is Pilate telling the Jewish leadership when he says, "What I have written, I have written," other than to say he is not going to change the inscription?

BEHOLD, YOUR MOTHER

40. What is the significance of our not knowing the identity of "the beloved disciple" at this point in the story?

THE LAST CUP

41. What is the significance of Jesus crying out, "My God, my God, why hast thou forsaken me?"

42. What is the significance of offering Jesus sour wine (or vinegar) to drink on the end of a piece of hyssop?

43. What is the significance of Jesus taking the sour wine and then pronouncing, "It is finished"?

44. What is the significance of the Temple curtain being torn in two after Jesus' death?

45. Why is it significant that when the soldiers came to Jesus, he was already dead, so they did not break his legs (cf. John 19: 32-33)?

46. The Apostles' Creed states, in part, Jesus

> *. . . suffered under Pontius Pilate,*
> *was crucified, died, and was buried.*
> ***He descended into hell;***   [Emphasis added]
> *on the third day he rose again from the dead. . . .*

St. Peter teaches Jesus "preached even to the dead, that though judged in the flesh like men, they might live in the spirit like God" (cf. 1 Peter 4: 6).

Who was waiting there for Jesus to preach to them and take them to heaven?

PONTIUS PILATE

47. What are two possible ends of Pilate's life?

THE CRUCIFIXION PSALM

48. Write down four parts of Psalm 22 that correspond to the various aspects of Jesus' death.

TEXT FROM PSALM 22	PART OF JESUS' DEATH IT PROPHESIES

VOCABULARY

Who or what am I?

1. _____ I come from a particular town in Galilee. I was on the inscription that Pilate ordered to be put on Jesus' cross.

2. _____ I will forever be known as the one who betrayed Jesus.

3. _____ I was pressed into service to help Jesus carry his cross on his way to

_____ (also known as _____).

4. _____ I was the Roman governor of Judea who handed Jesus over to be crucified.

5. _____ We were the governing council of the Jews who oversaw religious matters. Some of us were opposed to Jesus' crucifixion.

6. _____ I was thrown out of office by the Romans who gave my job to my son-in-law, whose name is _____.

7. From his judgment seat in the _____, Pilate sentenced Jesus to death by

_____.

8. _____ is the crime of insulting God or claiming to be God.

9. At the _____, instead of drinking _____, Jesus and the

apostles sang a hymn of praise before he went out to the garden of _____.

ADVANCED CONCEPTS:

JEWISH PASSOVER—CHRISTIAN EUCHARIST

At this point, we would do well to compare the Holy Week stories as follows:

- What the Jews would have been doing during the final week of Jesus' life (the Passover Tradition).

- How Jesus' last week on earth is explained by the Synoptic tradition

- How Jesus' last week on earth is explained by the Gospel of St. John (also referred to by scholars as the Johannine Tradition).

Jewish Passover Rite: Exodus 12: 1-13; 21-27.
Last Supper Stories: Matthew 26: 26-30, Mark 14: 22-26, Luke 22: 17-20, John 13: 1-14.
"The Real Presence": Mark 14: 22-24, John 6: 25-71, 1 Corinthians 10: 15-17, 11: 23-29

There is a major "contrast" between the accounts of the Last Supper between The Synoptic Gospels (Sts. Matthew, Mark, and Luke) and the Gospel of St. John. This is not to say that there is an error or deception. It is that each author wanted to stress a certain point. In the Synoptics, Jesus is specifically celebrating Passover. In the Gospel of St. John, the washing of feet is described as taking place "before the feast of Passover "during supper." The chain of events takes place thus:

	PASSOVER TRADITION	SYNOPTIC GOSPELS (STS. MATTHEW, MARK, & LUKE)	GOSPEL OF ST. JOHN
WEDNESDAY	Preparations are made for the Passover supper		Washing of the Feet at supper "before the feast of Passover"
WEDNESDAY NIGHT	- - - - -	- - - - -	Jesus is arrested
THURSDAY	Gathering for Passover supper		Jesus on trial
THURSDAY AFTERNOON	The Paschal Lamb is slaughtered		Jesus is crucified
THURSDAY NIGHT	Passover supper	The Last Supper; Jesus is arrested	Jesus is buried
FRIDAY	- - - - -	Jesus is crucified	first day in the tomb
FRIDAY EVENING	beginning of the Sabbath	Jesus dies and is buried; First day in the tomb	- - - - -
SATURDAY	Sabbath	second day in the tomb	second day in the tomb
SUNDAY MORNING	first day of the week	Resurrection!	Resurrection!

After studying this progression of events from Holy Week, answer the following questions.

- In the Synoptic Gospels, when does Jesus celebrate the Last Supper, and what does he do during this celebration?

- In the Gospel of St. John, when does Jesus celebrate the Last Supper, and what does he do during the celebration?

- The Synoptics obviously want us to know that Jesus transformed the Old Covenant of the Passover into the New Covenant of the Eucharist. St. John wants to teach us what the Eucharist *means* by telling us the story of Jesus washing the disciples' feet. What is this lesson?

- Lambs are a big theme in the writings of St. John (the Gospel and the Book of Revelation). Why does St. John's Gospel have Jesus dying on the cross on Thursday afternoon?

- Only in St. John, do we have the detail of the soldiers not breaking Jesus' legs, but piercing his side with a lance, to make sure he is dead. What connection is St. John making for us in recalling this detail of Jesus' death?

- Write a general statement as to how you would explain the contrast that exists between the Synoptic Gospels and St. John's Gospel.

Chapter 22: The Resurrection

THE RESURRECTION

1. Compared to what usually happened to the bodies of crucified men, what was noteworthy about what happened to Jesus' body after it was taken down from the cross?

2. Why did the chief priests ask Pilate to place a guard at the tomb of Jesus?

THE WOMEN WHO MET THE RISEN LORD

3. In the Synoptic Tradition, Jesus was buried on Friday immediately before the Sabbath. Why did the women come to Jesus' tomb bright and early "on the first day of the week" (i.e., after the Sabbath had passed)?

4. What did the women find when they arrived at Jesus' tomb?

THE ROAD TO EMMAUS: JESUS REVEALED IN THE EUCHARIST

5. Look at the following passages of Scripture, and circle the verbs:

    "And taking the five loaves and the two fish he looked up to heaven, and blessed, and broke and gave the loaves to the disciples . . ." (Matthew 14: 19 The Multiplication of the Loaves and Fish)

    "Now as they were eating, Jesus took bread, and blessed and broke it, and gave it to the disciples and said . . ." (Matthew 26: 26 The Last Supper)

    "When he was at table with them, he took the bread and blessed, and broke it, and gave it to them." (Luke 24: 30 The walk to Emmaus)

    "For I received from the Lord what I also delivered to you, that the Lord Jesus on the night when he was betrayed took bread, and when he had given thanks, he broke it and said, 'This is my body which is for you. Do this in remembrance of me.'" (1 Corinthians 11: 23-24 St. Paul's instruction on the Eucharist)

    These verses show that the Eucharist was a cornerstone teaching of Christianity from the beginning. Even when not specifically talking about the Eucharist (as in the stories of the Multiplication of the Loaves and Fish and the Walk to Emmaus), the Bible is still using Eucharistic language.

6. As the travelers made their way to Emmaus, Jesus, the very author of the Bible, explained it to them. How did they respond?

7. As evidenced by this story, reading the Bible alone does not seem to be enough to come to know Jesus. What is necessary?

THE POWER TO FORGIVE AND RETAIN SINS

8. Consider these passages from the Bible:

   "I will give you [St. Peter] the keys of the kingdom of heaven, and whatever you bind on earth shall be bound in heaven, and whatever you loose on earth shall be loosed in heaven." (Matthew 16: 19)

   "Truly I say to you [disciples], whatever you bind on earth shall be bound in heaven, and whatever you loose on earth shall be loosed in heaven." (Matthew 18: 18)

   We see the total giving Jesus has in mind for his Apostles. He entrusts everything to them, including his authority to announce God's forgiveness of sins. Why should a person go to confession, rather than only asking God to forgive their sins?

DOUBTING THOMAS

9. Tradition tell us that St. Thomas took the Gospel message as far as _____. In that country he still enjoys special honor and pious devotion.

10. While the earliest Christians did not have the cross as the sign of their faith, St. Thomas always carried a small wooden cross with him. What was the earliest sign of the Christian faith?

11. Why did St. Thomas carry the small wooden cross with him?

BACK TO GALILEE

12. Why did Jesus order the disciples to go back to Galilee?

13. What is the connotation of the 153 fish that the disciples caught?

PETER'S REDEMPTION

14. What is significant about the detail of the "charcoal fire" as Jesus and St. Peter meet after the Resurrection?

15. In the Greek language of the New Testament, there are a number of words for what we call "love." Two of these are *"philia,"* and *"agape"* (pronounced ah-GAH-pay).

    Philia means an emotional kind of love. This kind of love describes the feeling we have when we are spending time with someone we like.

    Agape is the fullest kind of love that Jesus himself has for us. It is a sacrificial kind of love that is born in the soul. It is a conscious decision to make a commitment and to live out that commitment to the end. It is the love that motivates people to make heroic sacrifices even to the point of death.

    "When they had finished breakfast, Jesus said to Simon Peter, 'Simon, son of John, do you love [**agape**] *me more than these?' He said to him, 'Yes, Lord; you know that I love* [**philia**] *you.' He said to him, 'Feed my lambs.' A second time he said to him, 'Simon, son of John, do you love* [**agape**] *me?' He said to him, 'Yes, Lord; you know that I love* [**philia**] *you.' He said to him, 'Tend my sheep.' He said to him the third time, 'Simon, son of John, do you love* [**philia**] *me?' Peter was grieved because he said to him the third time, "Do you love me?" And he said to him, 'Lord, you know everything; you know that I love* [**philia**] *you.' Jesus said to him, 'Feed my sheep.'"* (John 21: 15-17)

    We see in this very personal encounter between Jesus and St. Peter, our human reluctance to give ourselves completely over to God's idea of what love is. The first two times Jesus asks St. Peter if he loves him, he uses the word *agape,* what is he asking St. Peter?

When St. Peter answers, he says, "Lord you know that I *philia* you." What is St. Peter telling Jesus?

The third time Jesus asks the question, "Do you love me?" He gives in and uses *philia* himself. What is Jesus saying?

16. Why should this encounter between Jesus and St. Peter give us great hope?

VOCABULARY

Along with Nicodemus, _____ was one of the people who helped arrange for Jesus' burial by giving Jesus his own new tomb.

While St. _____ was the first of many people to see Jesus after he rose from the dead, there were no eyewitnesses to the _____ itself.

St. John tells us that the first time Jesus appeared to the disciples, and

St. _____ was not with them, he gave them his own authority to forgive sins. This is where Jesus instituted the Sacrament of _____.

On the evening of the day that Jesus rose from the dead, Jesus met _____ and a companion as they were walking to _____ about seven miles from Jerusalem.

Name _____

Date _____

Hour _____

Chapter 23: Jesus Fulfills the Old Testament

JESUS FULFILLS THE OLD TESTAMENT

1. The "suffering servant" that Isaiah describes is a _____ for Jesus. (*Hint: refer back to p. 38 of the text.*)

FULFILLING THE LAW AND THE PROPHETS

2. When Jesus promises to fulfill the Law and the Prophets, to what do most of his listeners think he is referring?

3. Explain briefly how Jesus' followers came to understand his teachings.

4. What is the relationship between knowing the New Testament and understanding the Old Testament?

5. How does Jesus fulfill the promises of the covenant made with Adam?

6. How does Jesus fulfill the promises of the covenant made with Noah?

7. How does Jesus fulfill the promises of the covenant made with Abraham?

8. How does Jesus fulfill the promises of the covenant made with Moses?

9. How does Jesus fulfill the promises of the covenant made with David?

THE CHURCH BEFORE JESUS

10. When does the history of the Church begin? Explain your answer.

11. The word "church" comes from the Latin word _____ and the Greek word

_____ which means _____.

12. Because we disobey God, we deserve _____. But it is God's plan not to lose any of us. Why then does God send his Son?

13. What was one of many reasons why the early Christian message spread so rapidly?

14. Even though people like Abraham, David, and the Prophets never received the Sacrament of Baptism, why did some early Church Fathers refer to them as Christians?

1. JESUS FULFILLS THE COVENANT WITH ADAM

15. What are three possible explanations for God referring to himself as "we" and "us" in the creation stories in the Book of Genesis?

    a.

    b.

    c.

16. How does the Trinitarian nature of God show through in his creation of humanity?

17. Genesis 3: 15 is often called the "Protoevangelium" which is a Latin word that means
_____. To what does this refer?

2. JESUS FULFILLS THE COVENANT WITH NOAH

18. Early Christians associated the Great Flood with _____.

19. Explain the relationship between the Great Flood of Noah's time and the forty days of Lent.

3. JESUS FULFILLS THE COVENANT WITH ABRAHAM

20. God promised _____ that all people would be blessed in him. This promise is
fulfilled in _____.

21. How had some of the promises made to Abraham already been fulfilled in the Old Testament?

4. JESUS FULFILLS THE COVENANT WITH MOSES

22. Moses prophesies in the Book of Deuteronomy that God would raise up another prophet like him.

    • What role does water play in the lives of both of these men?

    • What kind of freedom do both Jesus and Moses bring to their people?

THE NEW EXODUS

23. The Passover celebration looks _____ at deliverance from bondage in Egypt

    and _____ to the coming of deliverance brought by the Messiah.

24. Why is it noteworthy that Jesus would institute the Eucharist during the Passover meal?

JESUS THE PASSOVER LAMB

25. The Gospel of St. John presents the events of Jesus' death in a different light than the Synoptics. Why is it significant that in St. John's Gospel that . . .

... Jesus is handed over to be crucified at "about the sixth hour"?

... while the soldiers broke the legs of the men crucified with Jesus, when they came to him they did not break his legs?

5. JESUS FULFILLS THE COVENANT WITH DAVID

26. What is the New Kingdom of Israel?

27. What is the New Temple? Where is it found?

28. What *international aspect* of the covenant with David is perfectly fulfilled in Jesus?

29. In Jesus' time, how did many people mis-interpret the prophecies that applied to him?

VOCABULARY

- That we are baptized in the Name of the Father, and of the Son, and of the Holy Spirit is but one of many examples of the Christian belief in the _____.

- Non-Catholic Christians who seek to join the Catholic Church are called candidates for full communion; they are also known as _____. Those who have never been baptized are called _____.

- *"But now the righteousness of God has been manifested apart from law, although the _____ bear witness to it, the righteousness of God through faith in Jesus Christ for all who believe"* (Romans 3: 21-22).

- The adjective _____ describes the teachings, books, and other things that have to do with the leaders of Judaism.

- The Christian world can be depicted as a number of circles within a larger circle as below. The large circle that contains all others is Christianity. The smaller circles contained therein are the various denominations of Christians.

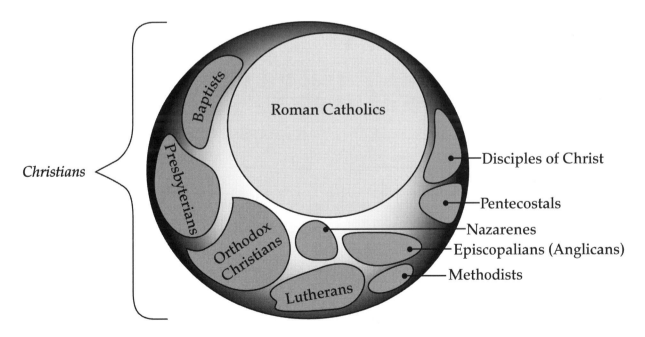

This diagram shows some of the more established Christian sects and have been chosen simply to make the point that all Catholics are _____, but not all _____ are Catholics.

Name _____

Date _____

Hour _____

Chapter 24: The Birth of the Church

THE BIRTH OF THE CHURCH

1. After Jesus rose from the dead, what was the last promise that he had to fulfill?

RESTORING THE KINGDOM

2. For _____ days after the Resurrection, Jesus remained on earth, teaching his disciples.

3. Of what did the ministry of the disciples consist?

4. Why did the disciples and Jesus' mother remain in Jerusalem between the Ascension of Jesus and Pentecost?

5. Once established, how is the "new" kingdom to be governed?

THE ELECTION OF MATTHIAS

6. Why did the eleven Apostles see a need to replace Judas?

7. Explain the relationship between the Apostles and the bishop of your diocese.

PENTECOST

8. The word "Pentecost" comes from the Greek word meaning _____.

9. What did the Jews celebrate during their feast of Pentecost?

10. When St. Peter and the rest of the Apostles began to speak in the many languages of the visitors who were in Jerusalem, what did their audience think?

11. God is joined to humanity through his Son, who is fully human and fully divine. How does this covenantal relationship endure until the end of time?

12. "The sacraments are efficacious signs of grace, instituted by Christ and entrusted to the Church, by which divine life is dispensed to us . . ." (CCC 1131). With this in mind, what does it mean to say that the Church is a "sacrament"?

PETER'S AUTHORITY

13. What does it mean that St. Peter, like Jesus, taught with authority?

14. What three activities identified the earliest Christian community in Jerusalem?

    a.

    b.

    c.

15. The chief priests were insulted that uneducated and common men would presume to teach them. What happened that kept them from taking action against the Apostles?

16. By what authority did St. Peter make the important decisions of the early Christian community?

THE MARTYRDOM OF STEPHEN

17. _____ was the earliest name for the Christian movement.

18. How was St. Stephen martyred?

19. What happened to the Christian community after the martyrdom of St. Stephen?

20. What was the net effect of the persecution of the Christian community?

21. _____ was a major figure in the persecutions of the Christians. He later became

known as St. _____.

WHAT THE EARLY CHRISTIAN COMMUNITY WAS LIKE

22. From the beginning, what set Christians apart as Christians?

23. Explain how the first Christians saw themselves.

24. After what significant event did the Jewish authorities finally expel the Christians from the Jewish faith?

25. How does the Mass still preserve the practice of the early Christians?

VOCABULARY

Study the vocabulary terms on page 441. These may appear on your chapter quiz.

Name _____

Date _____

Hour _____

Chapter 25: Reaching Out to All Nations

If you think about it, the Apostles followed a most predictable and reasonable course of action following Jesus' resurrection and ascension. They were Jews themselves, so they reached out to their fellow Jews, explaining how Jesus fit all the ancient prophecies perfectly. In this chapter we examine how the Apostles, to use a current term, are forced out of their "comfort zone" in taking Jesus' teachings to all people, and not just the Jews.

PHILIP BAPTIZES THE ETHIOPIAN

1. Eunuchs were men who had been castrated (i.e., had their testicles surgically removed). Mostly this would have been the case for men who were in charge of a king's harem of women. Since the eunuch would give up his masculinity for this job, they were highly paid and honored. This may have been the case with the Ethiopian eunuch (he appears to have been the treasurer of the queen of Ethiopia; a highly placed government official). Such mutilated people were not allowed to become Jews. What is the dilemma that St. Philip faced when this man asked to be baptized (cf. Acts 8: 36)?

2. How does St. Philip resolve the problem?

SAUL THE PERSECUTOR

3. Where was Saul born?

4. How would you describe Saul's ethnic background?

5. _____ was Saul's great Jewish teacher.

6. In what academic disciplines was Saul educated?

7. Aside from his good education, in what practical trade did Saul work?

8. Partly from extra biblical sources, and partly from his own writings, what do we know about Saul's physical person?

SAUL'S CONVERSION

9. Describe the main challenge Saul faced after his conversion with respect to his fellow Christians. How was this overcome?

10. Name the two Christians who helped Saul in his conversion to Christianity.

    a.

    b.

ARE CHRISTIANS JEWS?

11. Who were the "Proselytes at the Gate"?

12. Briefly explain St. Peter's own religious experience.

13. Given St. Peter's religious experience, along with the rest of the Apostles, what would seem to be the reasonable way for a Gentile to become a Christian?

14. As he engaged the Gentiles, how was St. Peter's way of thinking being challenged?

THE COUNCIL OF JERUSALEM

15. What were the three largest cities of the Roman Empire?

    a.

    b.

    c.

16. The city of _____ was the first great center of Christianity outside of Jerusalem.

17. In Antioch the followers of Jesus were for the first time called _____ (cf. Acts 11: 26).

18. We see in the Acts of the Apostles (10 and 11) that St. Peter had come to the conclusion that non-Jews could become Christians by simply being baptized. What awkward thing happened between St. Peter and his Gentile convert friends?

19. How does St. Paul respond to all of this (cf. Galatians 2: 11-14)?

20. Finally, the main figures in the early Church, St. Peter, the first pope; St. Paul, the Apostle to the Gentiles; and St. James the Bishop of Jerusalem resolve the issue once and for all as to what should be done with Gentiles who want to become Christians. How do they do it?

21. What was this meeting called?

VOCABULARY

_____ is the Jewish name for St. Paul who in addition to studying Greek literature and philosophy, studied the Hebrew Scriptures under the great Rabbi _____. St. Paul had been a zealous Pharisee who had an experience of the risen Christ while on his way to _____ where he intended to imprison Christians.

_____ was the first Christian to baptize a Gentile when he helped a _____ from _____ to understand the part of the Book of the Prophet Isaiah that he had been reading. This man was the treasurer of _____, the queen of his home country.

As the earliest Christians struggled to understand how to bring their faith to the rest of the world, St. Peter, also known by his Aramaic name _____, had the experience of seeing the Holy Spirit come upon the family of St. Cornelius, who was a Roman commander and a _____, which was the name of a person in the process of adopting the Jewish faith.

At the _____, Sts. Peter, _____, and _____ decided that the Gentiles would not have to become Jews before becoming Christians.

Name _____

Date _____

Hour _____

Chapter 26: Paul, An Apostle

1. What are the two miracles that most affected the early Christians?

    a.

    b.

PETER AND PAUL IN ACTS

2. What is St. Luke trying to prove about St. Paul in the Acts of the Apostles?

3. What is the comparison chart on page 460 trying to show us?

APOSTLE TO THE GENTILES

4. Make a list of at least four aspects of St. Paul's background that he used to his advantage as a proclaimer of the Gospel.

   a.

   b.

   c.

   d.

THE LAW WAS OUR CUSTODIAN

5. Explain what is meant by the Law as our Custodian or Pedagogue.

6. Does this mean that we are free to disregard things like the Ten Commandments? Explain.

SIN BRINGS DEATH THROUGH THE LAW

7. St. Paul does not propose that the Law of Moses be completely abandoned, yet he wants to show how we are freed from it. How does the Law of Moses bring condemnation to us?

8. What does "justified" or "justification" mean?

9. Why can we never earn justification through the Law of Moses?

ST. PAUL'S DOCTRINE OF JUSTIFICATION

10. How does God remedy the situation that we cannot earn justification for ourselves either through the Law of Moses or any other human means?

11. St. Paul tells us we are "saved by faith apart from works of the law" (Romans 3: 28). What does this mean?

12. Does St. Paul mean that if we have faith in Jesus we have no need to obey, for example, the laws of the Church, in order to go to heaven? Explain.

13. What critical piece of writing do we have from the New Testament that describes the relationship between faith and good works, and briefly, what does it say?

14. Why did Jesus have to die?

15. Using the framework of a family covenant, explain the connection between faith and good works.

ST. PAUL'S TRAVELS

16. St. Paul was very well traveled. Some traditions say he made it as far west as what modern day country?

17. How did St. Paul's status as a Roman citizen help him (cf. Acts 25: 1-12)?

18. While St. Paul was under house arrest in Rome, what did he do?

19. How, and where, did Sts. Peter and Paul finally meet their end?

VOCABULARY

Using the vocabulary word list for this chapter (text, p. 470), find each in the grid below.

```
A  V  P  G  Y  I  S  G  U  A  A  V  P  G  Y  G  M  B  J  K  G  L
Q  G  O  V  H  M  Z  P  J  Z  Q  G  O  V  H  T  A  U  V  L  L  F
A  H  I  C  A  K  X  J  A  V  A  H  I  C  N  Y  S  C  B  P  K  D
S  N  U  X  H  S  C  K  N  I  S  N  C  U  S  T  O  D  I  A  N  S
D  R  Y  S  J  F  I  L  H  R  N  S  Y  S  I  N  I  Z  T  Z  E  A
E  O  T  W  K  V  B  A  Y  T  E  A  T  F  K  M  K  A  S  S  R  Z
H  M  R  Q  L  B  N  N  T  M  H  P  I  Q  L  J  J  Q  W  D  O  V
G  E  E  A  P  G  M  B  F  K  G  C  E  A  P  E  A  P  K  X  J  M
H  K  W  Z  O  T  A  V  V  L  A  N  U  X  H  N  I  Z  T  Z  H  P
J  J  Q  P  J  Y  P  C  B  T  D  S  Y  S  J  M  K  A  S  S  G  L
T  I  M  O  T  H  Y  X  I  W  E  A  T  W  B  A  R  N  A  B  A  S
L  G  S  L  F  B  I  O  T  Z  H  P  R  Q  L  A  V  P  G  Y  J  J
P  F  D  K  D  M  N  A  S  S  G  L  E  A  P  Q  G  O  V  H  K  H
```

Name _____

Date _____

Hour _____

Chapter 27: The New Kingdom

1. What are the identifying factors in Jacob's (Israel's) prophecy to his son Judah that he made before he died?

2. How is this prophecy partially fulfilled in David, and then completely fulfilled in Jesus?

3. In Jesus, how are God's promises to Abraham and David fulfilled?

    Abraham:

    David:

THE SON OF DAVID

4. The New Testament begins with the Gospel of St. Matthew. How does that Gospel, and consequently the New Testament begin?

5. St. Matthew's genealogy (cf. ch. 18, pp. 322-324 of the text) is not just a list of names. He has some very specific points to convey about Jesus' family history. What are three of them?

    a.

    b.

    c.

6. The title "Son of David" is important because the Kingdom of _____ has replaced the Kingdom of _____.

7. St. Matthew is writing to a primarily Jewish audience. What is he trying to prove to them?

8. Briefly explain the history of the Canaanites, and why they were so hated by the Jews.

9. What does it mean when the Syro-Phoenician woman refers to Jesus as "Son of David"?

10. In St. Peter's Great Confession about Jesus in Matthew 16: 13-16, by which two titles of David does he refer to Jesus?

    a.

    b.

THE RIDDLE: HOW CAN DAVID'S SON BE DAVID'S LORD?

11. Jesus cites Psalm 110 to the Pharisees: *"The (a)*Lord *says to my (b)lord, Sit at my right hand, till I make your enemies your footstool."*

    To whom does *Lord* (a) refer?

    To whom does *lord* (b) refer?

12. What is St. Peter's point in citing the Prophet Joel in his sermon as found in Acts 2: 14-21?

13. At the end of St. Peter's sermon, how is the riddle answered?

THE CHURCH PERFECTLY FULFILLS THE DAVIDIC COVENANT

14. If Jesus is indeed the son of David, he must be the king of _____, but not

    in the sense of the small kingdom on the eastern shore of the Mediterranean Sea, but of

    _____ which is the _____.

THE DAVIDIC COVENANT: SEVEN PRIMARY FEATURES

15. How does Jesus complete each of the features of the Covenant that God made with David?

- Kingdom

- Dynasty

- God's own Son

- Unlimited in time and space

- Jerusalem

- The Temple

- Wisdom

THE DAVIDIC COVENANT: THREE SECONDARY FEATURES

16. Who is the Queen Mother of the New Kingdom?

17. Who is the Prime Minister or chief steward of the New Kingdom?

18. What is the "thank offering" of the New Kingdom?

VOCABULARY

Study the vocabulary terms on page 485. These may appear on your chapter quiz.

Name _____

Date _____

Hour _____

Chapter 28: The Catholic Church in Scripture

1. Who is responsible for the organizational structures of the Catholic Church?

ORGANIZATION OF THE CHURCH

2. What are the names of the three offices in the Church that took shape while the Apostles were still alive?

   a.

   b.

   c.

3. The _____ of the Church are the successors of the _____ with

   the _____ as their head and form a single _____.

4. Every Sunday at Mass, we say in the Nicene Creed, "...I believe in one, holy, Catholic, and apostolic Church ...." What do we mean when we say that the Catholic Church is "apostolic"?

THE PRIMACY OF PETER

5. Historically, what three events or criteria established St. Peter as the leader of the Church?

    a.

    b.

    c.

6. What is the name of the current successor of St. Peter?

COUNCILS OF THE WHOLE CHURCH

7. What is the name of the first Council of the Church? Where and when was it held (cf. ch. 25, p. 452 of the text)?

8. What is the name of the most recent ecumenical council of the Church? Where and when was it held?

SACRAMENTS

9. What is the definition of a sacrament as given in the *Catechism of the Catholic Church*?

BAPTISM

The text reminds us that, based on the teachings of Jesus himself (cf. John 3: 5), it is necessary to be baptized in order to go to heaven. This causes many serious questions to surface. Carefully read the following citations from the *Catechism of the Catholic Church* and answer the questions that follow.

1257 The Lord himself affirms that Baptism is necessary for salvation (cf. John 3: 5). He also commands his disciples to proclaim the Gospel to all nations and to baptize them (cf. Matthew 28: 19-20; cf. Council of Trent [1547] DS 1618; LG 14; AG 5). *Baptism is necessary for salvation for those to whom the Gospel has been proclaimed and who have had the possibility of asking for this sacrament* (cf. Mark 16: 16) {emphasis added]. The Church does not know of any means other than Baptism that assures entry into eternal beatitude [heaven]; this is why she takes care not to neglect the mission she has received from the Lord to see that all who can be baptized are "reborn of water and the Spirit." *God has bound salvation to the sacrament of Baptism, but he himself is not bound by his sacraments.*

1258 The Church has always held the firm conviction that those who suffer death for the sake of the faith without having received Baptism are baptized by their death for and with Christ. This *Baptism of blood,* like the *desire for Baptism,* brings about the fruits of Baptism without being a sacrament.

1259 For *catechumens* who die before their Baptism, their explicit desire to receive it, together with repentance for their sins, and charity, assures them the salvation they were not able to receive through the sacrament.

1260 "Since Christ died for all, and since all men are in fact called to one and the same destiny, which is divine, we must hold that the Holy Spirit offers to all the possibility of being made partakers, in a way known to God, of the Paschal Mystery" (GS 22 § 5; cf. LG 16; AG 7). Every man who is ignorant of the Gospel of Christ and of his Church, but seeks the truth and does the will of God in accordance with his understanding of it, can be saved. It may be supposed that such persons would have *desired Baptism explicitly* if they had known its necessity.

1261 As regards *children who have died without Baptism,* the Church can only entrust them to the mercy of God, as she does in her funeral rites for them. Indeed, the great mercy of God who desires that all men should be saved, and Jesus' tenderness toward children which caused him to say: "Let the children come to me, do not hinder them" (Mark 10: 14; cf. 1 Timothy 2: 4), allow us to hope that there is a way of salvation for children who have died without Baptism. All the more urgent is the Church's call not to prevent little children coming to Christ through the gift of holy Baptism.

- What if an adult was in the process of converting but suffered an untimely death?

- What about the people in parts of the world who have never even heard about Jesus?

- What about infants who die without being Baptized?

- What about the millions of unborn children every year who are aborted?

CONFIRMATION

10. Explain the two traditions for the Sacrament of Confirmation:

The Tradition of the Eastern Churches

The Tradition of the Western Churches

11. How are these two traditions attested to in Scripture?

12. What is the purpose of Confirmation? What does it accomplish?

EUCHARIST

13. How do we know that the bread and wine of the Eucharist truly become the Body and Blood, Soul, and Divinity of Jesus at the consecration at Mass?

14. The sacrifice of Christ on the cross is perpetually re-presented every time the Eucharist is celebrated. Jesus is not re-crucified or re-sacrificed. The following diagram shows that God exists in eternity, which means that he exists outside of time. What we call the past, present, and future, are all eternally present to God. This means that at any altar, in any church, when the priest is saying the words, "This is my Body; this is my Blood," *from God's point of view*, these words are being said simultaneously with Jesus as he said them for the first time. When the Gospel is proclaimed at Mass and we hear Jesus' words, *from God's point of view* these words are being spoken concurrently with Jesus as he spoke them for the first time. And, sadly, when we commit sin, our sins *from God's point of view*, are happening right as his Son is being nailed to the cross.

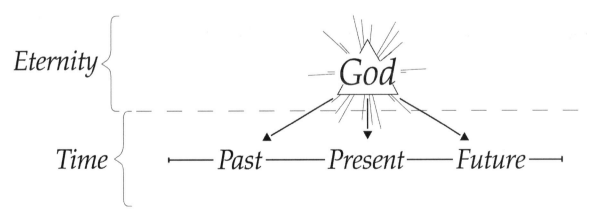

Is Jesus re-sacrificed at every Mass?

15. What is the term that the Church uses to describe the change of bread and wine into the Body and Blood of Jesus?

PENANCE

16. Where in the Bible does Jesus give his Apostles (the first bishops) his own authority to announce the forgiveness of sins?

17. _____ sin harms our relationship with God, while _____ sin

breaks our communion with him.

18. The prayer of absolution that the priest says over the penitent in confession goes like this:

    God the Father of mercies, through the death and resurrection of his Son has reconciled the world to himself and sent the Holy Spirit among us for the forgiveness of sins; though the ministry of the Church, may God grant you pardon and peace, and I absolve you from your sins, in the Name of the Father, and of the Son, and of the Holy Spirit. Amen.

    From the words of this prayer, on whose authority does the priest pronounce that the penitent's sins are forgiven?

ANOINTING OF THE SICK

19. It is no secret that many times when someone receives the Sacrament of the Sick, they do not recover from their illness. Sometimes they get worse, and sometimes they die. Why bother with this sacrament if people are not miraculously healed?

HOLY ORDERS

20. Write the meanings for the offices of service in the Church as taken from their Greek meanings:

    a. Bishop   _____

    b. Priest   _____

    c. Deacon   _____

21. _____ was one of the first deacons.

22. Elders or priests of the Church are mentioned in the Letter of James in connection with which sacrament?

MATRIMONY

23. What is the significance of Jesus being present at the wedding feast at Cana where he changed water into wine?

24. Where does the idea of marriage originate?

VOCABULARY

Match the following words to their definitions. You should be able to do this with your book closed.

____ Anointing of the Sick ____ Baptism ____ Confirmation

____ Council ____ Deacon ____ Eucharist

____ Holy Orders ____ Matrimony ____ Middle Ages

____ Paschal Mystery ____ Primacy ____ Reconciliation

____ Sacrament

A. A man who is ordained to assist the mission of the Church. From the Greek for "helper."

B. Christ's work of redemption accomplished principally by his Passion, death, Resurrection and Ascension.

C. This Sacrament conveys the outpouring of the Holy Spirit that was given to the Apostles at Pentecost.

D. The highest rank.

E. An outward sign instituted by Jesus Christ to confer the grace indicated by the sign.

F. The period between the end of the Roman Empire and the beginning of the Renaissance in which the Catholic Church was frequently the only force that preserved order.

G. The Sacrament that binds a man and woman in a life long covenant.

H. A meeting of the Church's leaders.

I. The Sacrament in which the guilt of Original Sin is washed away.

J. The Sacrament of the Body, and Blood, Soul and Divinity of Jesus Christ.

K. The Sacrament that forgives the guilt associated with sins committed after Baptism.

L. The Sacrament that ordains a man to lifelong service in the Church.

M. The Sacrament that, as the Letter of James teaches, heals and forgives sins.

Name _____

Date _____

Hour _____

Chapter 29: The End of History

1. What was the attitude of most early Christians about when the end of the world would come?

WHAT JESUS TAUGHT ABOUT THE END OF HISTORY

2. While the world (as in the physical universe in which we live) did not come to an end, in what sense did the world come to an end?

3. How will the end of the world affect persecutors and those who look for their reward in this world?

4. How will the end of the world affect Christians (and other men of good will) who have lived according to the New Law?

THE END OF THE OLD COVENANT

5. Describe the conditions in the world immediately before the end of the Old Covenant.

6. How did the Romans finally restore order in Judea?

7. What did the Christians do at this time?

SPECIAL NOTE

Many people complain that they have a hard time understanding the Book of Revelation. Others use it wrongly to make all sorts of bizarre claims and predictions.

Of the 440 verses in the Book of Revelation some 275 verses (63%) come either directly from, or refer to, the Old Testament (particularly from the Books of the Prophets Daniel and Ezekiel, with plentiful references to Genesis and Exodus). What do you think St. John is assuming about his audience?

So for people in our times, what do you think would be a major help in understanding the Book of Revelation?

---

8. What was the fate of the City of Jerusalem?

9. How did all of these tragic events fit with Jesus' predictions?

THE VISION OF THE HEAVENLY LITURGY

10. The highest form of worship for Western Catholics is called _____ and for Eastern

    Christians it is called _____.

11. St. John describes the heavenly liturgy in terms of things that we can see, hear, smell, feel, and
    taste. The earthly liturgy tries to copy the heavenly liturgy. From your own experience of going to
    Mass, describe things that we . . .

SEE	
HEAR	
SMELL	
FEEL	
TASTE	

12. Why does the Church use the things you mentioned above?

13. How is the Book of Revelation structured like the Mass?

THE LITURGY OF THE WORD

14. In the beginning of the Book of Revelation, St. John has a vision of "one like a son of man" (1: 13). Where do we first encounter this image in the Bible?

15. Jesus dictates seven letters to St. John that he is, in turn, to give to seven Christian communities (churches) that are located on the peninsula of Asia Minor. What else does it mean that St. John is to communicate these words of Jesus to "Seven Churches"?

16. A major theme of these letters is a call to repentance. This is similar to what part of the Mass?

17. A scroll is a piece of rolled up parchment. The seals are wax that is dripped along the seam and then pressed with the symbol of the sender's signet ring. When St. John sees the scroll with seven seals (which represents the will of God), it is given to the Lamb that was slain, who begins to open the scroll, one seal at a time. What happens when the Lamb opens the first seal (Revelation 6: 1-8)?

18. Revelation 7 contains one of the most misused pieces of Scripture. It refers to 144,000 who are "saved." Some groups, like the Jehovah's Witnesses, take this literally to mean that there are only 144,000 souls in heaven. According to the text, historically, who are represented by the 144,000?

19. St. John explains 12,000 of each of the twelve tribes of Israel are "marked." How is the message also meant for us?

20. When the seventh seal is opened, seven angels blow seven trumpets releasing plagues upon the earth. To what does this refer?

THE HEAVENLY EUCHARIST

21. What great artifact from Israel's history shows up in Revelation 11?

22. Read the text of Revelation 12: 1-2 (it is reproduced at the bottom of page 512 of the text). Since the woman is the mother of the Messiah, who might this be?

23. What does the crown of twelve stars on the woman's head represent?

24. Fill in the following table.

THE HISTORICAL ARK OF THE COVENANT CONTAINED . . .	WHICH CORRESPONDS TO . . .

25. So what, or who, is St. John showing us to be the New Ark of the Covenant?

26. Way back in Genesis 3: 15, we saw what we have called the *protevangelium* or the "first Gospel." How does Revelation 12 fulfill this Gospel?

THE BEASTS

27. St. John makes frequent use of the image of "beasts" in the Book of Revelation. The beast in Revelation 13 is described as having ten horns, seven heads, and ten diadems.

    The horns are symbols of _____.

    The diadems are symbols of _____.

    The seven heads refer to the seven hills of Rome.

    What are the two interpretations as to what the beast signifies?

28. The number "666" has been the subject of many claims that the number means the devil. Many anti-Catholic propagandists claim that it means the pope. Read Revelation 13: 18 very carefully either from your Bible, or where it is reproduced at the bottom of page 514 of the text. What does the biblical text *itself* tell you about the meaning of the number "666"?

THE NEW JERUSALEM

29. What is the real message of the Book of Revelation?

30. With its glorious description of the New Jerusalem, the Book of Revelation offers us a glimpse of a joyous and perfect world of happiness and praise of God. How and where do we get a taste of the New Jerusalem in the here and now?

THE WARNING AND PROMISE

31. We often hear of people claiming to have figured out when the end of the world will come. They use the Book of Revelation, the prophecies of Nostradamus, and any number of other superstitions. What is the bottom line, the final answer, on this question from the lips of Jesus himself?

32. What, for Christians, is the warning and promise of the Book of Revelation?

VOCABULARY

Study the vocabulary terms on page 521. These may appear on your chapter quiz.

Name _____

Date _____

Hour _____

Chapter 30: How to Read the Bible

THE BIBLE IS LITERATURE

1. When we say that the Bible is *literature,* what do we mean?

2. Since the Bible is also *ancient literature* what is necessary for us to do if we wish to properly understand it?

3. What is meant by the *literal* sense of Scripture?

4. Give a few examples of the literal sense of some pieces of Scripture.

5. Jesus says in the Gospel of St. Matthew (23: 9), *"And call no man your father on earth, for you have one Father, who is in heaven."*

What is the literalist interpretation of this verse?

What is the Catholic sense of this verse?

SPIRITUAL SENSES

6. What is meant by the *spiritual* sense of scriptural interpretation?

7. What is the *allegorical* or *typical* sense?

8. What is an example of the *allegorical* or *typical* sense?

9. What is the *moral* or *topological* sense?

10. What is an example?

11. What is the *analogical* sense?

12. What is an example?

13. All of these senses are based on what?

LOOK TO THE CHURCH FOR GUIDANCE

14. The marks of the Catholic Church are One, Holy, Catholic, and Apostolic. How does the unity of the Catholic Church prove that the Church, through the Magisterium, is the one true interpreter of Scripture?

15. What two practical resources do Catholics have at their disposal to understand the Bible?

WHAT TO READ FIRST

16. If a Christian is completely new at studying the Bible, where is a good place to start reading?

PRAY

17. What are the two ways in which the Word of God comes to us?

    a.

    b.

18. How does participation at Mass help us to read and understand the Bible?

Catholic Prayers and Devotions

In any endeavor, there are certain basics that must be learned, memorized, and internalized.
These prayers and devotions are fundamental to the life of an active, practicing Catholic.

The Ten Commandments

1. I am the Lord your God: You shall not have strange gods before me.
2. You shall not take the name of the Lord your God in vain.
3. Remember to keep holy the Lord's day.
4. Honor your father and your mother.
5. You shall not kill.
6. You shall not commit adultery.
7. You shall not steal.
8. You shall not bear false witness against your neighbor.
9. You shall not covet your neighbor's wife.
10. You shall not covet your neighbor's goods.

The Precepts of the Church
[See CCC #2042-2043, Second Edition, 1997]

1. You shall attend Mass on Sundays and holy days of obligation and rest from servile labor.
2. You shall confess your sins at least once a year.
3. You shall receive the Sacrament of the Eucharist at least during the Easter season.
4. You shall observe the days of fasting and abstinence established by the Church.
5. You shall help provide for the needs of the Church.

The Corporal Works of Mercy

- Feeding the hungry
- Giving drink to the thirsty
- Clothing the naked
- Sheltering the homeless
- Visiting the sick
- Visiting the imprisoned
- Burying the dead

The Spiritual Works of Mercy

- Counseling the doubtful
- Instructing the ignorant
- Admonishing sinners
- Comforting the afflicted
- Forgiving offenses
- Bearing wrongs patiently
- Praying for the living and the dead

The Gifts of the Holy Spirit

- Wisdom
- Understanding
- Counsel
- Fortitude
- Knowledge
- Piety
- Fear of the Lord

Theological Virtues

- Faith
- Hope
- Charity

The Sins that Cry to Heaven

- The murder of the innocent (cf. Genesis 4: 10)
- Homosexual behavior (cf. Genesis 18: 20, 19: 13)
- The enslavement of people (cf. Exodus 3: 7-10)
- Oppression of the widow, orphan, or alien (cf. Exodus 22: 21-24)
- Withholding wages from the laborer (cf. Deuteronomy 24: 14-15)

"The catechetical tradition recalls that there are *'sins that cry to heaven'*: the blood of Abel; the sin of the Sodomites; ignoring the cry of the people oppressed in Egypt and that of the foreigner, the widow, and the orphan; injustice to the wage earner" (CCC 1867).

Capital Sins

- Pride
- Covetousness
- Lust
- Anger
- Gluttony
- Envy
- Sloth

Opposed Virtues

- Humility
- Liberality
- Chastity
- Meekness
- Temperance
- Brotherly love
- Diligence

Cardinal Virtues

- Prudence
- Justice
- Fortitude
- Temperance

The Beatitudes   (Matthew 5: 3-12)

- Blessed are the poor in spirit, for theirs is the kingdom of heaven.
- Blessed are those who mourn, for they shall be comforted.
- Blessed are the meek, for they shall inherit the earth.
- Blessed are those who hunger and thirst for righteousness, for they shall be satisfied.
- Blessed are the merciful, for they shall obtain mercy.
- Blessed are the pure of heart, for they shall see God.
- Blessed are the peacemakers, for they shall be called the sons of God.
- Blessed are those who are persecuted for righteousness' sake, for theirs is the kingdom of heaven.
- Blessed are you when men revile you and persecute you and utter all kinds of evil against you falsely on my account. Rejoice and be glad, for your reward is great in heaven.

The Sign of the Cross

In the name of the Father, and of the Son, and of the Holy Spirit. Amen.

The Lord's Prayer

Our Father, who art in heaven, hallowed be thy name. Thy kingdom come; thy will be done on earth as it is in heaven. Give us this day our daily bread; and forgive us our trespasses as we forgive those who trespass against us; and lead us not into temptation, but deliver us from evil. Amen.

The Hail Mary

Hail, Mary, full of grace, the Lord is with thee; blessed art thou among women, and blessed is the fruit of thy womb, Jesus. Holy Mary, Mother of God, pray for us sinners, now and at the hour of our death. Amen.

The Glory Be (The Doxology)

Glory be to the Father, and to the Son, and to the Holy Spirit. As it was in the beginning, is now, and ever shall be, world without end. Amen.

Morning Offering

O Jesus, through the Immaculate Heart of Mary, I offer you my prayers, works, joys, and sufferings of this day for all the intentions of your Sacred Heart, in union with the holy sacrifice of the Mass throughout the world, in thanksgiving for your favors, in reparation for my sins, for the intentions of all my relatives and friends, and in particular for the intentions of the Holy Father. Amen.

Consecration to the Blessed Virgin Mary

My Queen and my Mother, I give myself entirely to you, and, in proof of my affection, I give you my eyes, my ears, my tongue, my heart, my whole being without reserve. Since I am your own, keep me and guard me as your property and possession. Amen.

Act of Faith

O my God, I firmly believe that you are one God in three divine Persons, Father, Son, and Holy Spirit; I believe that your divine Son became man and died for our sins, and that he shall come to judge the living and the dead. I believe these and all the truths that the holy Catholic Church teaches, because you have revealed them, who can neither deceive nor be deceived.

Act of Hope

O my God, relying on your almighty power and infinite mercy and promises, I hope to obtain pardon for my sins, the help of your grace, and life everlasting, through the merits of Jesus Christ, my Lord and Redeemer.

Act of Charity

O my God, I love you above all things, with my whole heart and soul, because you are all-good and worthy of all love. I love my neighbor as myself for the love of You. I forgive all who have injured me and ask pardon of all whom I have injured.

Prayer to One's Guardian Angel

Angel of God, my guardian dear, to whom God's love commits me here, ever this day (night) be at my side, to light and guard, to rule and guide. Amen.

The *Angelus*   (Said outside the Easter Season)

V. The Angel of the Lord declared unto Mary;

R. And she conceived by the Holy Spirit.

Hail Mary . . .

V. Behold the handmaid of the Lord.

R. Be it done unto me according to your word.

Hail Mary . . .

V. And the Word was made flesh,

R. And dwelt among us.

Hail Mary . . .

V. Pray for us, O holy Mother of God.

R. That we may be made worthy of the promises of Christ.

V. Let us pray.
Pour forth we beseech you, O Lord, your grace into our hearts, that we, to whom the incarnation of Christ, your Son, was made known by the message of an angel, may by his passion and cross be brought to the glory of his resurrection, through the same Christ our Lord.

R. Amen.

Regina cæli   (Said during the Easter Season)

V. Queen of Heaven, rejoice! Alleluia.

R. For he whom you did merit to bear. Alleluia.

V. Has risen, as he said. Alleluia.

R. Pray for us to God. Alleluia.

V. Rejoice and be glad, O Virgin Mary. Alleluia.

R. For the Lord is truly risen. Alleluia.

V. Let us pray.
O God who gave joy to the world through the resurrection of your Son, our Lord Jesus Christ, grant, we beseech you, that through the intercession of the Virgin Mary, his Mother, we may obtain the joys of everlasting life, through the same Christ our Lord.

R. Amen.

Prayer to the Holy Spirit

V. Come, O Holy Spirit, fill the hearts of your faithful and enkindle in them the fire of your love. Send forth your Spirit, and they shall be created.

R. And you shall renew the face of the earth.

V. Let us pray.
O God, who has taught the hearts of the faithful by the light of the Holy Spirit, grant that by the gift of the same Spirit we may be always truly wise and ever rejoice in his consolation. Through Christ our Lord.

R. Amen

Eternal Rest

V. Eternal rest grant unto them (him/her), O Lord,

R. And let perpetual light shine upon them (him/her).

V. May they (he/she) rest in peace.

R. Amen.

V. May their (his/her) soul(s) and the souls of all the faithful departed, through the mercy of God, rest in peace.

R. Amen.

Blessing Before A Meal

Bless us, O Lord, and these your gifts, which we are about to receive from your bounty, through Christ our Lord. Amen.

Thanksgiving After A Meal

We give you thanks, almighty God, for all your benefits, who live and reign forever and ever. Amen.

The Apostles' Creed

I believe in God, the Father almighty, creator of heaven and earth. I believe in Jesus Christ, his only Son, our Lord. He was conceived by the power of the Holy Spirit and born of the Virgin Mary. He suffered under Pontius Pilate, was crucified, died, and was buried. He descended into hell. On the third day he rose again. He ascended into heaven, and is seated at the right hand of the Father. He will come again to judge the living and the dead. I believe in the Holy Spirit, the holy Catholic Church, the communion of saints, the forgiveness of sins, the resurrection of the body, and life everlasting. Amen.

Fatima Prayer

O my Jesus, forgive us our sins, save us from the fire of hell, draw all souls to heaven, especially those who are in most need of your mercy. Amen.

Hail Holy Queen

Hail, holy Queen, Mother of mercy, our life, our sweetness, and our hope. To you do we cry, poor banished children of Eve. To you do we send up our sighs, mourning and weeping in this valley of tears. Turn then, most gracious advocate, your eyes of mercy towards us, and after this exile show unto us the blessed fruit of your womb, Jesus. O clement, O loving, O sweet virgin Mary.

V.   Pray for us, O holy Mother of God.
R.   That we may be made worthy of the promises of Christ.

Rosary Prayer

O God, whose only-begotten Son, by his life, death, and resurrection, has purchased for us the rewards of eternal life; grant, we beseech you, that, we, who meditate on these mysteries of the most holy Rosary of the Blessed Virgin Mary, may imitate what they contain, and obtain what they promise. Through Christ our Lord. Amen.

The *Memorare*

Remember, O most gracious Virgin Mary, that never was it known that anyone who fled to your protection, implored your help, or sought your intercession was left unaided. Inspired with this confidence, I fly unto you, O Virgin of virgins, my Mother. To you I come, before you I stand, sinful and sorrowful. O Mother of the Word incarnate, despise not my petitions, but in your mercy hear and answer me. Amen.

Act of Contrition

O my God, I am heartily sorry for having offended you, and I detest all my sins, because I dread the loss of heaven and the pains of hell; but most of all because they offend you, my God, who are all good and deserving of all of my love. I firmly resolve, with the help of your grace, to confess my sins, to do penance, and to amend my life. Amen.

Prayer to St. Michael

Saint Michael the Archangel, defend us in battle; be our defense against the wickedness and snares of the devil. May God rebuke him, we humbly pray. And do you, O prince of the heavenly host, by the power of God thrust into hell Satan and all the evil spirits who prowl about the world for the ruin of souls. Amen.

How to Pray the Rosary

1. Holding the Crucifix in your hand, make the Sign of the Cross and pray the Apostles' Creed.
2. On the first bead after the Crucifix, pray the Our Father.
3. Pray one Hail Mary on each of the next three beads, asking God to increase faith, hope, and charity in your life.
4. On the bead after these three, pray the Glory Be, announce the First Mystery, and pray the Our Father.
5. Pray one Hail Mary for each of the ten following beads, and end them by praying the Glory Be and the Fatima Prayer.
6. Announce the Second Mystery and repeat steps four and five. Do the same for the Third, Fourth, and Fifth Mysteries.
7. After the Fatima Prayer for the Fifth Mystery, pray the Hail Holy Queen, the Rosary Prayer, and end with the Sign of the cross.

The Mysteries of the Rosary

The Joyful Mysteries

1. The Annunciation
2. The Visitation
3. The Nativity
4. The Presentation
5. The Finding of Jesus in the Temple

The Luminous Mysteries

1. The Baptism of Christ in the Jordan
2. The Manifestation of Christ at the wedding of Cana
3. The Proclamation of the Kingdom of God, with his call to conversion
4. The Transfiguration
5. The Institution of the Eucharist

The Sorrowful Mysteries

1. The Agony in the Garden
2. The Scourging at the Pillar
3. The Crowning with Thorns
4. The Carrying of the Cross
5. The Crucifixion

The Glorious Mysteries

1. The Resurrection
2. The Ascension
3. The Descent of the Holy Spirit
4. The Assumption
5. The Coronation of the Blessed Virgin Mary